Collins

Introduction to
Secondary
Science

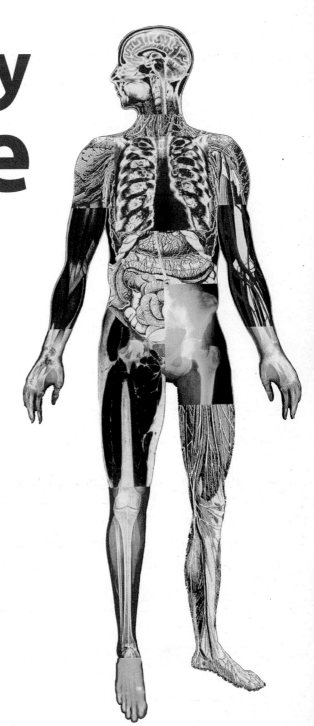

Chris Sherry
Louise Smiles
Brian Cowie

Student Book

William Collins' dream of knowledge for all began with the publication of his first book in 1819. A self-educated mill worker, he not only enriched millions of lives, but also founded a flourishing publishing house. Today, staying true to this spirit, Collins books are packed with inspiration, innovation and practical expertise. They place you at the centre of a world of possibility and give you exactly what you need to explore it.

Collins. Freedom to teach

Published by Collins
An imprint of HarperCollinsPublishers
77–85 Fulham Palace Road
Hammersmith
London
W6 8JB

Browse the complete Collins catalogue at:
www.collinseducation.com

© HarperCollinsPublishers Limited 2011

10 9 8 7 6 5 4 3 2 1

ISBN 978-0-00-741517-5

British Library Cataloguing in Publication Data
A Catalogue record for this publication is available from the British Library

Commissioned by Hanneke Remsing
Project managed by Hanneke Remsing and Caroline Green
Edited by Vicki Harley
Proofread by Camilla Behrens
Design and illustrations by Ken Vail Graphic Design
Picture research by Caroline Green
Cover design by Julie Martin
Production by Arjen Jansen

Printed and bound by L.E.G.O. S.p.A. Italy.

CONTENTS

How to use this book

This Collins student book is filled with exciting and relevant science to support you throughout your course. While you work through the different biology, chemistry and physics topics look out for the features highlighted below and use them to build your skills and knowledge.

Be inspired by people explaining how they use science in their careers with introductions that put every topic in context. Science isn't only for scientists!

Learn your essential biology, chemistry and physics with clear explanations, photographs and diagrams.

Avoid common mistakes by checking the Remember boxes to see what students often get wrong – and make sure you get it right.

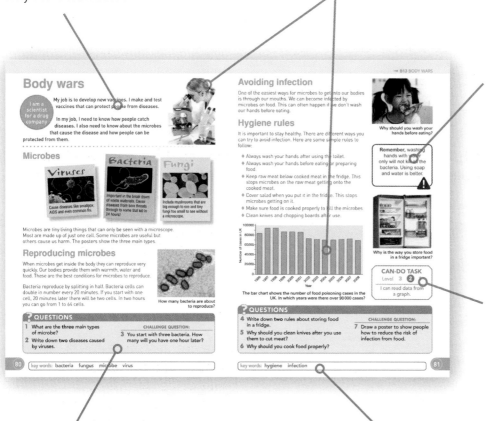

Put what you've learnt into practice by trying the activities in the Can-Do boxes.

Check you have understood the section before you move on by answering the questions on each page, including a challenge question to really get you thinking.

Make sure you understand the scientific language by checking the key words at the bottom of each page.

Build your practical skills with tasks that show you how to plan, carry out and analyse scientific experiments.

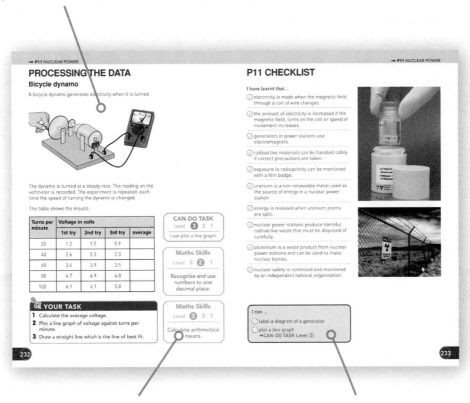

See what maths you need to use where Maths Skills are highlighted.

Find out how much you have learnt at the end of each topic to by reading through the summary checklist. Look back over the topic to remind yourself of anything you have forgotten.

If you are unsure of any of the scientific words you come across in this book look them up in the glossary where you'll find a clear explanation.

BIOLOGY

Dead or alive

I am a personal trainer

My job is to help people get fit and stay healthy. I help people by showing them different exercises they can do. I also work out a fitness programme for them to follow.

In my job, I need to know about the different organs in the body. This helps me to understand and plan exercises people can do to improve fitness of different parts of their bodies.

Life processes

Humans are living things. All living things carry out the seven life processes listed below.

1 growth – living things can get bigger
2 nutrition – living things need food
3 reproduction – living things have young
4 movement – even plants can move
5 sensitivity – this is reacting to things like touch
6 excretion – getting rid of waste
7 respiration – releasing energy from food.

Which life process resulted in this baby elephant?

? QUESTIONS

1 Write down the seven processes of living things.

2 What is the meaning of the word 'excretion'?

CHALLENGE QUESTION:

3 How does oxygen get from the lungs to the heart?

---

key words: excretion   nutrition   reproduction   respiration   sensitivity

Body systems

The human body needs body systems in order to carry out life processes. Each body system is made up of one or more organs.

Some body systems are described in the table.

Body system	Main organs in body system	Job of body system
circulatory	heart and blood vessels	transports food and oxygen in the blood
digestive	stomach and intestine	breaks down food so it can get into the blood
respiratory	lungs	take in oxygen from the air

Organ transplants

Organs can sometimes stop working and need replacing.

Some healthy organs can be removed from a dead person and transplanted to a living person.

♦ The dead person is called the donor.
♦ The living person is called the host.

When an organ is removed from the donor it needs to be kept cold to stop it decaying.

Once the new organ has been transplanted into the host it can be rejected.

Some people want to donate organs when they die. These people carry organ donor cards.

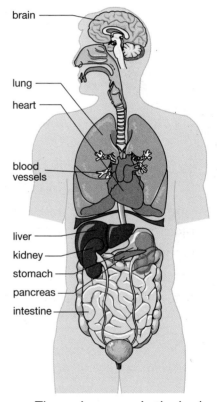

The main organs in the body.

? QUESTIONS

4 Write down the main organs in the circulatory system.

5 Why do some people carry organ donor cards?

6 When an organ is taken from a body for a transplant it is kept cold. Explain why.

CHALLENGE QUESTION:

7 Look at the diagram showing the organs in the body. Which organ could be donated by a living person?

key words: body system   donor   host   organ   transplant

Cells

All living things are made of cells.

As your body grows it needs to make new cells.

The diagram and micrograph show the parts of an animal cell.

New cells are also needed if the old ones are damaged, for example when you get a cut.

New cells are made when cells divide.

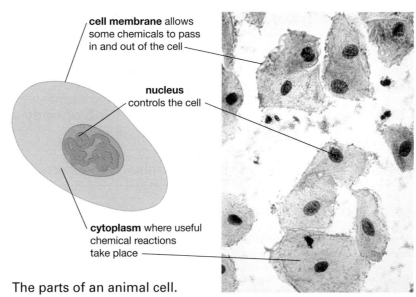

cell membrane allows some chemicals to pass in and out of the cell

nucleus controls the cell

cytoplasm where useful chemical reactions take place

The parts of an animal cell.

Animal cells seen under a microscope. Which part controls the cell?

Pulse rate

Your heart beats to pump blood around the body.

You can measure how fast your heart beats by counting your pulse rate. Place your fingers on your wrist just below your thumb. You should feel your pulse moving blood through the artery.

During exercise your pulse rate goes up. After exercise your pulse rate goes back to normal. The time it takes to get back to normal is called your recovery time.

The fitter you are the quicker your recovery time.

How quickly your breathing rate gets back to normal is another measure of recovery time and how fit you are.

> **Remember,** animal cells don't have cell walls!
>
>

? QUESTIONS

8 Write down the part of the cell where useful chemical reactions take place.

9 How does the body make new cells?

10 Finish this sentence:

The time it takes your pulse rate to get back to normal after exercise is called your …… time.

CHALLENGE QUESTION:

11 Describe **one** way you could measure recovery time.

key words: cell   cell membrane   cytoplasm   nucleus   pulse rate   recovery time

Exercise

When you exercise your muscles contract to move your body.

When muscles contract they need energy. The more you exercise the more energy your muscles need.

Energy comes from glucose (sugar) in food. Respiration is a process that takes place in every living cell. It releases the energy in food.

For the process of respiration to work it needs oxygen. As you exercise your muscles need more oxygen.

To get more oxygen into the body your breathing rate goes up.

Your pulse rate also goes up because your heart pumps faster in order to get more oxygen to your muscles. The oxygen is carried around the body in the blood.

Sometimes when we exercise we can injure ourselves. Warming up before exercise and warming down after exercise reduces the chance of injury.

Why does your breathing rate go up during exercise?

Remember, energy comes from food, not oxygen.

CAN-DO TASK

Level 3 2 **1**

I can measure a person's breathing rate or pulse.

❓ QUESTIONS

12 Write down the gas needed in respiration.

13 Why do muscles need energy?

14 Why is it important to warm up before playing football?

CHALLENGE QUESTION:

15 Kim measures her pulse rate before and after exercise. Her pulse rate before exercise is 72 beats per minute. Her pulse rate after exercise is 112 beats per minute.

a) Calculate the amount by which Kim's pulse rate goes up.

b) Explain why her pulse rate goes up. Use ideas about muscles and oxygen in your answer.

key words: energy   muscle   oxygen   respiration   warm down   ⟹ warm up

PLANNING TO COLLECT DATA
Exercise and heart rate

When you exercise your heart rate goes up. This happens because your muscles are working harder and need more energy. To get more energy they need more oxygen. A faster heart rate means blood can take oxygen to the muscles quicker.

You can measure your heart rate by counting your pulse. Count the beats in 15 seconds and multiply by 4 to get your pulse rate over 1 minute.

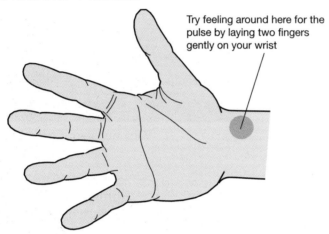

Try feeling around here for the pulse by laying two fingers gently on your wrist

How much your heart rate goes up depends on how hard you work. Running needs more energy than walking. This means your heart rate will go up more when you run.

 YOUR TASK

Write a plan to find the effect of different types of exercise on heart rate. Read the information and use it to help you write your plan.

1 The length of time you exercise can also affect your heart rate. How will you make sure you exercise for the same amount of time?

2 What else do you need to do to make this a fair test?

3 What will you measure to get your results?

4 How will you know if you have recovered from one exercise before you start the next?

5 How will you make sure your experiment is safe?

6 Write out your plan as a step-by-step list.

MATHS SKILLS

Level **3** **2** **❶**

Take measurements using a stop-clock.

B1 CHECKLIST

I have learnt that ...

- ✓ the life processes are growth, nutrition, reproduction, movement, sensitivity, excretion and respiration.

- ✓ the circulatory, respiratory and digestive systems are needed for the life processes.

- ✓ new body cells needed for growth are made when cells divide.

- ✓ respiration is the release of energy from glucose using oxygen.

- ✓ muscles need energy when they contract.

- ✓ heart rate goes up during exercise so that muscles get more oxygen.

- ✓ recovery time after exercise is linked to fitness.

- ✓ some healthy organs can be taken from a donor and transplanted into a host.

- ✓ transplanted organs can be rejected.

- ✓ people can choose to carry an organ donor card.

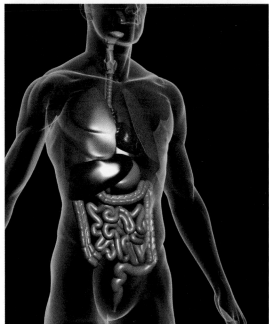

I can ...

- ✓ label the nucleus, cytoplasm and cell membrane.

- ✓ measure a person's breathing rate or pulse
  ➡ CAN-DO TASK Level ①.

- ✓ interpret data on breathing and pulse rate.

- ✓ label the lungs, heart, kidneys and liver on a diagram of the body.

Babies

I am a midwife

My job is to help women during pregnancy and to be there when their babies are born.

In my job, I need to know about how the baby develops inside the womb. I also need to be able to monitor the baby and mother's health before, during and after birth.

Reproductive organs

Males and females have different reproductive organs.

The female makes eggs in her ovaries (singular ovary).

The male makes sperm in his testes (singular testis).

Fertilisation

When a male releases sperm into the vagina of a female fertilisation can take place.

Fertilisation is the point when the sperm fuses with the egg. This normally happens in the oviduct.

The fertilised egg develops into a foetus. The foetus grows into a baby.

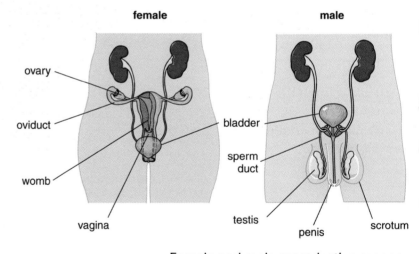

female   male

ovary
oviduct
womb
vagina
bladder
sperm duct
testis
penis
scrotum

Female and male reproductive organs.

? QUESTIONS

1 Write down the part of a female where the eggs are made.

2 What is the meaning of the word 'fertilisation'?

CHALLENGE QUESTION:

3 Where does fertilisation normally take place?

key words: egg   fertilisation   foetus   ovary   oviduct   sperm   testis   womb

Pregnancy

When the egg starts to develop into a foetus a woman is said to be pregnant.

One of the first signs of pregnancy is that a woman's periods stop. She will also start to gain weight.

Antenatal care

During pregnancy, women meet with the midwife at the antenatal clinic. This is where tests are carried out to make sure the baby is growing properly.

To check the mother's health and the baby's progress the midwife measures the mother's blood pressure, weight and height. The midwife can also look at ultrasound scans to check how the foetus is growing.

Why is the mother's weight monitored during pregnancy?

Twins

Sometimes a woman can have more than one baby at a time.

- ◆ If two eggs are fertilised then she will have non-identical twins.
- ◆ Identical twins develop when one fertilised egg splits in two at the start of pregnancy.

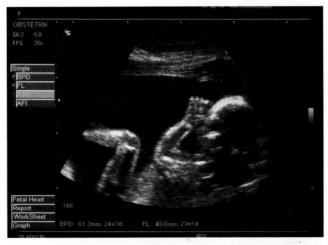

This is an ultrasound image of a foetus in the mother's womb. Why are these scans taken?

> **Remember,** only one sperm enters an egg – you can't get twins by two sperm entering one egg.

? QUESTIONS

4 Write down **two** tests a midwife might carry out on a pregnant woman.

5 What happens to a woman's periods when she is pregnant?

6 Which type of twins develop from one egg?

CHALLENGE QUESTION:

7 Find out why blood pressure is monitored during pregnancy.

key words: antenatal   identical twin   non-identical twin   pregnant

Inside the womb

As the foetus grows inside the womb it needs to be protected and fed.

- ◆ The placenta is where oxygen and food move from the mother's blood into the blood of the foetus. Waste materials move from the foetus's blood into the mother's blood to be excreted by the mother.
- ◆ The cord carries the blood to and from the placenta.
- ◆ The bag of water protects the foetus from knocks.

Birth

When the baby is ready to be born the woman goes into labour.

The muscle wall of the womb contracts giving the woman labour pains.

The woman's waters break (water flows out of the womb).

The contractions increase as the muscle wall starts to push the baby out of the womb.

After the baby is born the placenta is pushed out. This is called the afterbirth.

Some time after her baby's birth, the woman's periods will start again.

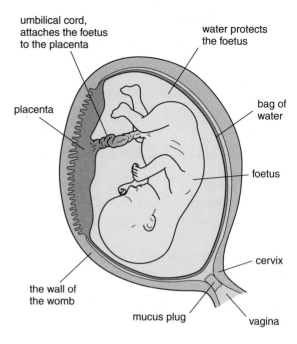

umbilical cord, attaches the foetus to the placenta

water protects the foetus

placenta

bag of water

foetus

cervix

the wall of the womb

mucus plug

vagina

A foetus inside the womb.

> **Remember,** the mother's blood does not mix with the blood of the foetus – there are membranes to keep them separate. ⚠

❓ QUESTIONS

8 Finish the sentence.

The placenta is where ...... and food passes into the foetus's blood.

9 What causes labour pains?

10 Finish the sentence.

After the baby is born the placenta is pushed out as the ....

CHALLENGE QUESTION:

11 The growing foetus makes waste like carbon dioxide. Find out how the waste is removed from the foetus.

key words: afterbirth bag of water cord foetus labour placenta

Growing babies

After they are born, babies are monitored to check they are growing properly.

They may also have other checks like hearing and sight. Look at the record card. It shows the record for one baby born on the 9th February.

WEIGHT RECORD (birth to 2 yrs)

Date	Weight	Weight gain	Comments
9/2/05	3.82 kg	birth weight	
20/2/05	4.10 kg	0.28 kg	
19/3/05	4.85 kg	0.75 kg	reflexes ok
16/4/05	5.12 kg	0.27 kg	small weight gain
14/5/05	5.54 kg	0.42 kg	
11/6/05	5.95 kg		hearing, sight ok

Weight record card for a baby.

Growing population

Every second at least three babies are born somewhere in the world. This means the world population is going up and up. The graph shows how much it has changed.

People need resources like homes, food, clean water and fuel. The more people there are the more resources we need. If the population keeps on going up we will run out of some resources.

People also make waste like sewage and household rubbish. We are running out of places to put all the rubbish we make.

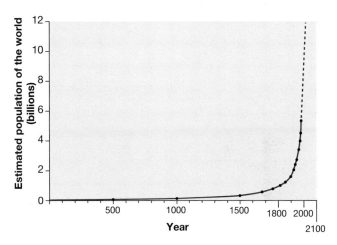

Graph showing the world population from year 0 to 2100.

CAN-DO TASK

Level 3 **2** 1

I can read data from a graph.

? QUESTIONS

12 Look at the record card.

  a) What did the baby weigh on the 20th of February?

  b) What is the weight gain for the 11th of June?

  c) Draw a graph of the baby's weight gain from birth until the 11th of June.

13 Write down one resource that might run out if the population gets too high.

CHALLENGE QUESTION:

14 Plastic household waste is more of a problem than paper waste. Suggest a reason why.

key words: household waste   population   resource

PATTERNS IN DATA
Growth curves

A baby's weight is measured at birth. Every few months a nurse will check the baby's weight. This is done to find out if the baby is making good progress.

The graph shows the weight of one baby.

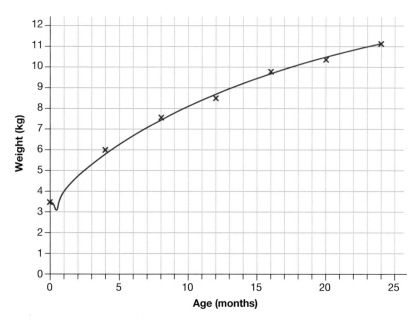

How a baby's weight goes up can depend on its health and diet. If the baby's weight is less than expected then the nurse may become concerned.

YOUR TASK

Use the information to answer these questions.

1 Describe the pattern in the data.

2 How much does the baby weigh at birth?

3 How old is the baby when it weighs 6 kg?

4 When is the baby growing the fastest? Choose from the list.

　　0–4 months　　4–8 months　　16–20 months

5 Most babies aged 24 months are between 12 kg and 15 kg. The nurse is concerned about the baby in the graph. Explain why.

MATHS SKILLS

Level　3　**2**　1

Read data from charts and graphs.

B2 CHECKLIST

I have learnt that ...

- the sperm are made in the testes and eggs are made in the ovaries.

- fertilisation is when an egg and a sperm join.

- a fertilised egg develops into a foetus.

- identical twins develop from the same egg and non-identical twins develop from two eggs.

- when a woman is pregnant her periods stop and she gains weight.

- during pregnancy the mother has her blood pressure, weight and height measured.

- when her waters break and she gets labour pains a woman knows she is in the early stages of labour.

- the placenta is lost as afterbirth.

- a woman's periods begin again after childbirth.

- the human population is increasing.

- a higher human population means we need more resources like clean water and fuel.

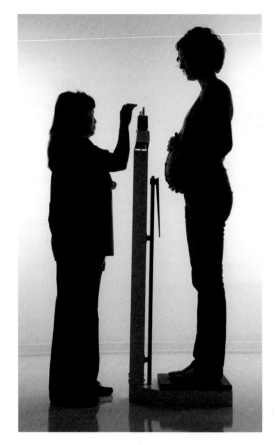

I can ...

- label the female reproductive organs on a diagram.

- label the male reproductive organs on a diagram.

- label the placenta, cord, foetus and bag of water on a diagram.

- interpret data from babies' growth.

- interpret data on human population size.

- read data from a graph
  ➡ **CAN-DO TASK Level ②**.

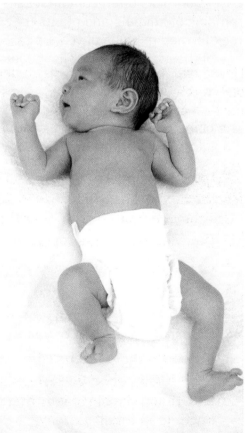

Extinction

I am a palaeontologist (fossil hunter)

My job is to search rocks to find fossils. I travel all around the world as I look for the best fossils.

I spend time breaking apart rocks to see if they contain remains of animals and plants from millions of years ago. I need to know about how fossils formed. I can use fossils to explain what life was like when the animals and plants were alive. The fossils may also help explain why some animals became extinct.

Fossils

Over millions of years, rock forms in layers. When different rocks are found in layers, the oldest rock is usually at the bottom.

Layers of rocks often contain fossils. The fossils are remains of animals and plants that were alive when the rock formed millions of years ago. Scientists can tell the age of the rock by the fossils it contains.

What happened to the skin that covered the bones of this dinosaur fossil?

How fossils are made

The biggest fossils found are normally the remains of dinosaurs. This is how they formed:

♦ The dinosaur died and the soft body parts rotted away.
♦ The hard bones and teeth were covered by many layers of sand or mud.
♦ Slowly the bones and teeth turned into stone fossils.

CAN-DO TASK

Level 3 2 **1**

Given information, I can match an animal to where it lives or when it lived.

? QUESTIONS

1 Finish these sentences.

Dinosaurs lived ...... of years ago.

Scientists know this because the remains of the dinosaurs are found as ....

2 Describe the main stages that happen when a dinosaur becomes a fossil.

CHALLENGE QUESTION:

3 Explain why most fossils only show the bones and teeth of the dead animal.

key words: extinct   fossil   rock layer

Frozen life

Stone fossils are not the only remains of living organisms.

♦ Mammoths have been found frozen in ice.
♦ Some insects became trapped in tree sap which turned into amber.
♦ In America many dinosaur remains have been found preserved in tar pits.

How did this dragonfly become a fossil?

Life on Earth

The Earth is about 4600 million years old. Scientists think that life began on Earth about 3500 million years ago.

Life started out as tiny microscopic organisms. These organisms changed into lots of different types of animals or plants. Each different type became a new species. A species is a type of animal that looks similar and can breed with each other.

As time passed some species died out and others developed.

The animals and plants we find today are a result of the many changes that have taken place over millions of years.

The way in which living things change over time is called evolution.

Remember, a new species does not appear over night. It can take millions of years for a new species to develop. ⚠

Ancient species

Fossils show how living things have changed over time. Scientists have found that some animals have been around for millions of years without changing much. One example is the crocodile. There were crocodiles on Earth when the dinosaurs were alive. The crocodile species alive then were very similar to the ones that are alive now.

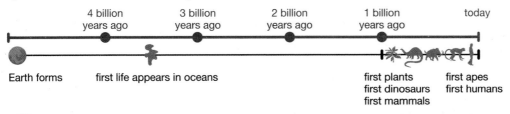

| 4 billion years ago | 3 billion years ago | 2 billion years ago | 1 billion years ago | today |

Earth forms   first life appears in oceans   first plants   first apes
                                                       first dinosaurs   first humans
                                                       first mammals

? QUESTIONS

4 Fossils found in ice still have their soft parts. Suggest why the soft parts have not rotted away.

5 How many years ago did life on Earth start?

6 What word is used to describe the changes to life on Earth over millions of years?

CHALLENGE QUESTION:

7 Fossils are used to identify living things from the past. Suggest why we do not know about all the species that ever lived on Earth.

key words: evolution   species

Variation

The fossils of dinosaurs show us that they came in all shapes and sizes. Some dinosaurs like the Tyrannosaurus Rex were meat eaters with large sharp teeth. Apatosaurus was a dinosaur with a long neck to reach leaves high in trees.

The Tyrannosaurus Rex and the Apatosaurus were different species, which is why they looked very different.

Even dinosaurs of the same species showed slight variation. Some Apatosaurus dinosaurs had longer necks than others. This meant they were better adapted at reaching leaves higher in trees.

Why was a long neck important to the Apatosaurus?

Competition

Dinosaurs, like the animals of today, needed to compete to survive. They would have competed with other dinosaurs for shelter, food and even a mate.

When competing for food the fastest and strongest often got more food. They survived and passed on their features to the next generation.

Why would sharp teeth help with competition for food?

? QUESTIONS

8 Finish the sentences about variation. Choose words from this list.

> die   different   shorter   survive

Members of the same species are all slightly ......; they show variation.

Some might be taller or ...... than others.

Those with the best features are more likely to ....

9 Write down **three** things animals compete for.

10 Foxes eat rabbits. How do you think being able to run fast helps a rabbit survive?

CHALLENGE QUESTION:

11 Plants collect water from the soil through their roots.

A plant with longer roots is better adapted for living in dry soil then a plant with short roots.

Explain why.

key words: adaptation   competition   species   variation

Extinction

There are no dinosaur species on Earth now. They are all extinct. Other animals that have died out are the sabre-toothed tiger and the dodo.

One species of sabre-toothed tiger lived in the grasslands of North America. The place where a species lives is called its habitat. Sabre-toothed tigers were adapted to hunt food in the grasslands. Scientists think the species died out because 10 000 years ago the habitat got much colder. The sabre-tooth could not adapt to the changes and became extinct.

The Dodo *(Didus ineptus).*

The dodo. Do you know, or can you find out, why it became extinct?

Endangered

Every hour a species becomes extinct somewhere in the world. Animals and plants close to extinction are said to be endangered. Endangered species include the giant panda, the gorilla and the primrose flower.

Species are endangered when their numbers are so low the whole species could die out. Humans have caused many species to become endangered or even extinct. The reasons include destruction of habitats, hunting and producing too much pollution.

The giant panda only eats bamboo. Why might this be a disadvantage to the survival of the panda?

CAN-DO TASK

Level 3 **2** 1

I can collect (scientific) information about an endangered or extinct species.

? QUESTIONS

12 Write down what is meant by the word 'extinct'.

13 Write down **three** reasons why a species might become extinct.

14 Look at the table. It shows the world population of some animal species.

Animal	Giant panda	Tiger	African elephant	Polar bear
World population	2500	3200	500 000	20 000

a) Which of these animals is the **most** endangered?

b) Which animal is **less** likely to become extinct?

CHALLENGE QUESTION:

15 Humans have helped increase the number of elephants in the world.

Suggest ways humans can help endangered animals.

key words: endangered   extinct   habitat

PROCESSING THE DATA
Endangered birds

Red kites are large birds that feed on dead animals. They became extinct in England around 150 years ago. Humans thought they were pests and killed them. In fact they were useful because they kept the streets free of rotting food.

Year	Number of breeding pairs
2000	3
2001	8
2002	10
2003	16
2004	24
2005	33
2006	40
2007	47
2008	69

Red kites survived in Wales but were endangered. They have now returned to many parts of England.

In 1999 red kites were introduced into Yorkshire. Since then their numbers have been recorded each year.

The table shows the number of breeding pairs found in Yorkshire between 2000 and 2008.

✎ YOUR TASK

1 Draw a bar graph of the data.
Make sure:
- you label the axes
- use a suitable scale
- draw the bars at the correct height
- give your graph a title

2 Describe the pattern in the graph.

3 Suggest **two** reasons why the numbers of red kites are changing.

MATHS SKILLS

Level 3 2 **1**

Draw a bar chart.

B3 CHECKLIST

I have learnt that ...

- ✓ fossils can tell us about animals and plants that lived a long time ago.

- ✓ when animals die the soft parts rot but the teeth and bones can become fossils.

- ✓ animals and plants can be preserved in ice, amber and tar pits.

- ✓ life on Earth began about 3500 million years ago.

- ✓ evolution describes how living things have changed over millions of years.

- ✓ living things compete for shelter, food and mates, and the fittest survive.

- ✓ a habitat is the place where an animal or plant lives.

- ✓ some species may become extinct because of hunting, pollution or their habitat being destroyed.

- ✓ pandas, gorillas and primroses are all endangered species.

- ✓ the dodo, sabre-toothed tigers and dinosaurs are extinct.

I can ...

- ✓ describe how fossils form.

- ✓ identify variation in animals or plants.

- ✓ interpret data on the population size of an endangered animal.

- ✓ match an animal to where it lives or when it lived
  ➡ CAN-DO TASK Level ①.

- ✓ collect (scientific) information about endangered or extinct species
  ➡ CAN-DO TASK Level ②.

Casualty

I am a paramedic

My job is to give emergency first aid to people.

I respond to emergency calls and treat people before they are taken to hospital.

In my job, I need to know about how to treat a casualty in an emergency. Sometimes I may need to restart their heart to keep them alive. I also need to know how the heart works and how the blood is moved around the body.

Emergency first aid

Oxygen is needed to keep the body alive. The blood takes oxygen from the lungs to the rest of the body. If someone stops breathing or loses a lot of blood, they could die. This is why important checks are made at the scene of an accident.

If you see an accident, this is what you should do:

♦ First find out who is injured. If help is needed, call for an ambulance.
♦ Explain to the emergency services where you are and what has happened.
♦ If you have first aid training, you can follow the emergency first aid code called the ABC code.

ABC code

A = Airways – check the nose and mouth are not blocked.

B = Breathing – are they breathing? If not, you can give them mouth-to-mouth resuscitation.

C = Circulation – do they have a pulse? If their heart has stopped, they need CPR (cardiopulmonary resuscitation).

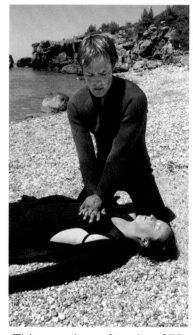

This man is performing CPR. Why is it important to keep the heart working?

? QUESTIONS

1 Why is it important that a casualty keeps breathing?

2 What number would you call in an emergency?

CHALLENGE QUESTION:

3 Find out how to do CPR.

key words: ABC code   airway   blood   breathing   circulation   oxygen

RICE code

If you damage soft tissue, for example the muscles in your ankle, use the RICE code to know what to do.

R = rest the injured ankle.
I = ice, put ice on the injury for 20 minutes every hour.
C = comfortable support, strap the ankle with a bandage.
E = elevate, keep your foot up on a chair when resting it.

The heart

◆ The heart pumps the blood around the body. There are two sides to the heart. This is why the heart is called a double pump.

◆ The right side of the heart pumps blood to the lungs.

◆ In the lungs oxygen enters the blood and carbon dioxide leaves the blood.

◆ The blood then returns to the left side of the heart.

◆ The left side then pumps the blood around the body.

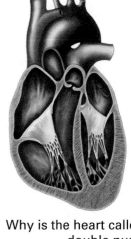

Why is the heart called a double pump?

The heart is made of muscle which contracts to push the blood out. To keep working the heart muscles need oxygen. A blood vessel called the coronary artery keeps the heart muscle supplied with blood and oxygen.

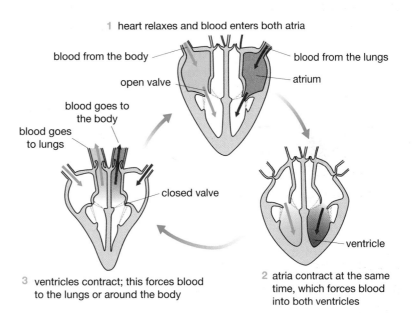

1 heart relaxes and blood enters both atria

blood from the body — open valve

blood from the lungs — atrium

blood goes to the body
blood goes to lungs — closed valve

ventricle

3 ventricles contract; this forces blood to the lungs or around the body

2 atria contract at the same time, which forces blood into both ventricles

How the heart acts as a double pump.

❓ QUESTIONS

4 Write down the four stages of the RICE code.

5 Which side of the heart pumps blood to the lungs?

6 Why does heart muscle need a good blood supply?

CHALLENGE QUESTION:

7 Explain why the heart has valves inside it.

key words: blood   coronary artery   elevate   heart   ice   oxygen   rest   RICE code

Blood vessels

Blood is carried around the body in blood vessels. There are three main types of blood vessels.

♦ Arteries – carry the blood away from the heart to the rest of the body.

♦ Veins – carry blood from the body to the heart.

♦ Capillaries – are tiny blood vessels that link arteries and veins.

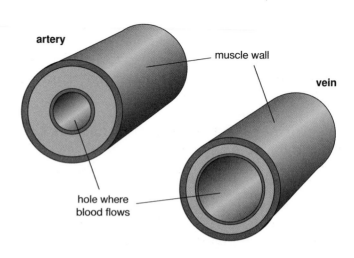

artery

muscle wall

vein

hole where blood flows

Arteries and veins carry blood around the body.

> **Remember, A**rteries carry blood **A**way from the heart, not to it. ⚠

Damaged blood vessels

If you cut your finger and it starts to bleed slowly, the chances are you have damaged lots of tiny blood capillaries. The cut will soon form a scab and you will lose very little blood.

If you damage arteries or veins then you can lose a lot of blood. The blood in the artery is under high pressure. If you cut an artery, blood is lost very quickly. To stop the bleeding you would need to put pressure on the cut until it is stitched up.

The body can cope with less than 10% blood loss. Someone who loses more than 30% of their blood may need a blood transfusion.

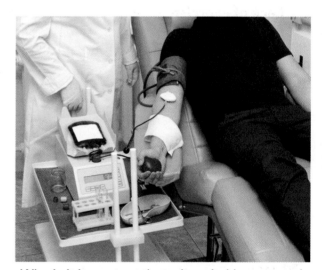

Why is it important that a hospital has a supply of blood?

❓ QUESTIONS

8 Which type of blood vessel carries blood to the heart?

9 Which is the smallest type of blood vessel?

10 Why is cutting a vein more dangerous than cutting a capillary?

CHALLENGE QUESTION:

11 An adult has 5 litres of blood in their body. How much could their body cope with losing?

key words: artery   blood transfusion   capillary   vein

A healthy heart

More and more people are damaging their heart because of the way they live. High-fat diets, smoking and not enough exercise can cause some people to have heart attacks.

The high level of fat in their diet can block the artery that supplies the heart with oxygen. The muscles of the heart get less oxygen and become damaged. This causes heart disease.

There are many ways that people can damage their heart:

- ◆ **Smoking** damages the lungs. Chemicals in cigarette smoke also make the heart beat more quickly all the time.
- ◆ As we get **older** out hearts begin to weaken.
- ◆ People who are **overweight** put a strain on their heart. The blood has to travel further around their body than in thinner people.
- ◆ Sometimes a fatty substance coats the inside walls of **blood vessels**. This makes the blood vessel narrower. The heart has to work much harder to pump blood along it.
- ◆ **Lack of exercise** means muscles go flabby. Since the heart is made of muscle it can get weaker if it becomes unfit. Exercise encourages the heart to grow and develop.

To help prevent heart disease there are three things a person can do:

- ◆ exercise
- ◆ eat less fat
- ◆ not smoke.

Why should a person not eat too much fat?

> **Remember,** not everyone who is overweight and smokes will get heart disease. It just increases the chance that they will.

❓ QUESTIONS

12 Write down **three** ways you can help keep your heart healthy.

13 Why is smoking bad for your heart?

CHALLENGE QUESTION:

14 John and Adil are discussing the effect of diet on health.

John: Fatty food does not harm you. My granddad ate lots of burgers and lived until he was 80.

Adil: Fatty food does harm you. Scientists have studied hundreds of people and found eating fatty food means you are more likely to get heart disease.

a) Who thinks fatty food causes heart disease, John or Adil?

b) Who has better evidence for his argument, John or Adil? Explain your answer.

key words: exercise   fat   heart disease   smoking

REVIEWING THE METHOD
Smoking and exercise

If you smoke then you find it harder to breath when you exercise

Mark and Ceri are talking about smoking and exercise.

To find out who is correct Mark and Ceri investigate exercise and breathing rate. They ask six friends to help them.

This is their method.

I don't think it makes any difference and I can prove it

- ◆ Each person sits still for 2 minutes.
- ◆ They then count how many times they breathe in for 1 minute.
- ◆ They exercise by running on the spot for 2 minutes.
- ◆ Some of their friends run faster than the others.
- ◆ They sit down and count their breaths in 1 minute again.

The table shows their results.

Name	Age	Smoker, yes or no	Number of breaths in 1 minute before exercise	Number of breaths in 1 minute after exercise	Increase in breaths in 1 minute
Anne	16	no	8	12	4
Bill	15	no	5	10	
Peter	25	no	6	14	
Jill	38	no	7	16	
Sue	45	yes	8	18	
Wesley	21	yes	6	8	

 YOUR TASK

1 Calculate the increase in breaths for each person. Anne has been done for you.

  a) Who had the highest breathing rate at the end of the experiment?

  b) Are they a smoker?

2 Mark tells Ceri the results prove he is right. But Ceri thinks their method was not a fair test. Write down **two** reasons why the method was not a fair test.

3 How could they improve their method?

4 Wesley runs 800 m for a local athletics club. Explain why his results may not be valid.

MATHS SKILLS

Level **3** 2 1

Carry out simple calculations involving +, −, ×, ÷.

B4 CHECKLIST

I have learnt that ...

- the body needs a supply of oxygen to stay alive.
- the ABC code is airway, breathing and circulation.
- the RICE code is followed when soft tissue is damaged.
- the heart is a muscle that pumps blood around the body.
- heart muscle needs a supply of oxygen.
- arteries carry blood away from the heart and veins take blood to the heart.
- cutting a vein or artery could cause more blood loss than cutting a capillary.
- someone who loses more than 30% of their blood may need a transfusion.
- heart disease can be caused by a blocked artery.
- people who exercise are less likely to get heart disease.

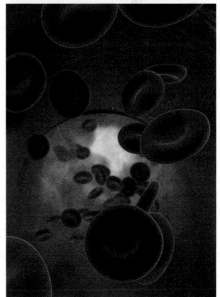

I can ...

- call for help in an emergency.
- follow the ABC code in an emergency.
- follow the RICE code if someone has a soft tissue injury.

Healthy eating

I am a footballer

My job is all about being fit and healthy so that I can play my best football.

I spend time with a nutritionist who helps me plan what I eat.

In my job, I need to know about different types of food and the energy they provide. I need to be able to balance my diet so that my muscles stay strong. I also need to know about vitamins and minerals to keep healthy so that I stay on the team.

Balanced diet

People are all made up of the same chemicals. Most of our body is water; the rest is mainly protein, fats and carbohydrates. We also contain small amounts of vitamins and minerals.

To stay healthy we need all the different food types in the table.

Food type	Why we need it	Foods that contain it
carbohydrates	give us energy	bread, potato, rice, pasta
fats	give us energy	butter, milk, chocolate
proteins	used to grow and repair tissue	meat, beans, cheese
vitamins	keep us healthy	fruit and vegetables
minerals	for strong bones and healthy blood	milk, meat
water	stops dehydration	water, milk, tea, juice

> **Remember,** foods contain different food types. A cheese sandwich contains fat, protein and carbohydrates.

? QUESTIONS

1 What are the six types of food in a balanced diet?

2 Write down **three** foods that contain fat.

CHALLENGE QUESTION:

3 Write down what you ate yesterday and list the food types it contained.

key words: carbohydrate   fat   mineral   protein   vitamin   water

Special diets

Everybody is different. We all need different diets depending on our lifestyles.

Footballers use more energy than people working in offices. So footballers need to eat more carbohydrates. Carbohydrates can be starch or sugar. Food with starch in is better for a footballer because the energy lasts longer. Footballers also need more protein for their muscles to be repaired and grow bigger. Fat is also a source of energy.

Teenagers will need more protein than adults because they are still growing.

Which foods would you eat to help you grow?

Problem diets

Sometimes people eat more food than they need. The extra energy they take in is stored in the body as fat. Too much fat leads to a person being overweight. There are health risks to being overweight, for example heart disease.

Eating too little is also a problem. Underweight people also risk damaging their body.

In many poor countries people do not get enough protein. This leaves them very weak and unhealthy.

Diet and exercise

To stay as healthy as possible we need to eat a balanced diet and exercise. Exercise helps keep our muscles and heart strong. Exercising also uses energy, which means we can eat more food.

Why do some children not get enough protein?

CAN-DO TASK

Level **3** 2 1

I can record my daily protein intake.

? QUESTIONS

4 Dan is 15 and plays rugby in his spare time.

Colin is 15 and watches TV in his spare time.

Who do you think needs to eat more carbohydrates? Explain your answer.

5 Why is being underweight unhealthy?

6 Why do we need to exercise to stay healthy?

CHALLENGE QUESTION:

7 Some children only get rice to eat. Why is only eating rice a problem?

key words: diet energy overweight protein underweight

Food labels

Many people like to know about what they are eating. This is because they want a diet that is right for them.

Food labels help people check what they are eating.

People who want to lose weight will look for the energy content in the food. This helps them balance the energy they take in with the energy they use. Food with less fat in will contain less energy.

Someone with heart disease needs to eat less salt. Food labels tell you how much salt is in the food.

Athletes need a high protein diet so they will look for the protein content in food.

Energy	275kJ
	65kcal
Protein	3.4g
Carbohydrate	4.7g
of which sugars	4.7g
Fat	3.6g
of which saturates	2.3g
mono-unsaturates	1.0g
polyunsaturates	0.1g
Fibre	0.0g
Sodium	trace
Salt equivalent	trace

How much protein is in this food?

Food tests

You can find out what is in food by doing some simple tests. Chemicals are added to the food. If the food type is present the chemicals change colour.

The table shows you the different food tests.

Food type	Test – chemical added	Colour change
starch	add brown iodine solution	turns blue-black
sugar (glucose)	add blue Benedict's solution and heat	turns brick red
protein	add blue biuret solution	turns violet

CAN-DO TASK
Level   3   2   **1**

I can safely carry out a food test for starch.

CAN-DO TASK
Level   3   **2**   1

I can safely carry out a food test for glucose.

? QUESTIONS

8 Look at the picture of the food label.

  a) Which type of carbohydrate is in the food, starch or sugar?

  b) Someone with a heart problem could eat this food. Explain why.

9 Look at the table of food tests. Iodine solution is added to food containing starch. What colour does it go?

CHALLENGE QUESTION

10 How could you show that cheese contains protein?

key words: food label   food test   protein   starch   sugar

The digestive system

Food must be digested before it can be absorbed into the blood. Digestion means to break food down into smaller molecules.

Digestion takes place in the gut. This is the name of the tube that takes the food from the mouth to the anus.

Enzymes

Enzymes are chemicals in the body that speed up reactions. The enzymes in your gut speed up the digestion of food. Food is turned from large, insoluble materials into small, soluble chemicals. Soluble food can be absorbed into the blood.

The **mouth** breaks food down into smaller lumps. Saliva helps breaks starchy food down to sugar.

Acid and enzymes in the **stomach** break down the protein. The acid kills any bacteria in the food. Here the food is a watery sludge.

The **small intestine** breaks down foods. It can also absorb food into the blood.

The **large intestine** absorbs water from the food. The waste food becomes more solid.

The **rectum** stores the remaining waste. The ring of muscle in the anus holds the waste in the body until you go to the toilet.

The steps in digestion.

Different food, different enzyme

Each type of food needs a different enzyme to break it down. The enzyme in your mouth can only break down starch. A different enzyme in your stomach breaks down protein. Your small intestine has many different enzymes; each one digests a different food type.

> **Remember,** the acid in your stomach helps the enzyme work. The acid itself does not digest the food. ⚠

❓ QUESTIONS

11 List the parts of the gut that food passes through from the mouth to the anus.

12 Are the enzymes for digesting protein found in the mouth or the stomach?

13 Where in the gut is food absorbed into the blood?

CHALLENGE QUESTION:

14 Draw a flow chart to show what happens to food in the gut. Start in the mouth and finish with the food passing into the blood.

key words: absorb   digestion   enzyme   gut   soluble

PLANNING TO COLLECT DATA
Sugar test

We eat food to give us energy. Some foods are healthier than others. Food with lots of sugar in can be bad for us.

It is possible to compare the amount of sugar in food using Benedict's solution.

Add a small amount of food to Benedict's solution and heat it.

If the Benedict's solution changes colour then the food contains sugar. Different colours indicate different amounts of sugar.

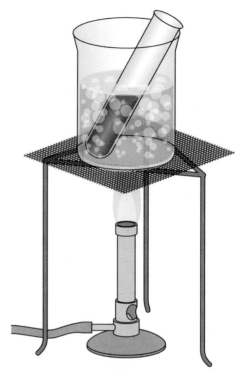

Testing a food sample for sugar using Benedict's solution.

	Amount of sugar		
	Low	Medium	High
Colour of Benedict's solution when heated	green	yellow	brick-red

YOUR TASK

Read the information and use it to help you write a plan to compare the amount of sugar in different foods.

1 How will you heat up the Benedict's solution safely?

2 The time you leave the food in the hot Benedict's solution may also affect the colour.

3 How will you make sure you heat it for the same amount of time?

4 What else do you need to do to make this a fair test?

5 What will you look for to get your results?

6 How will you make sure your experiment is safe?

7 Write out your plan as a step-by-step list.

B5 CHECKLIST

I have learnt that ...

- ✓ a balanced diet contains: water, carbohydrates, proteins, fats, vitamins and minerals.

- ✓ a poor diet could make you overweight or underweight.

- ✓ if you are overweight or underweight it could cause you to be unhealthy.

- ✓ exercise helps you stay healthy.

- ✓ different people need different diets because they have different lifestyles.

- ✓ teenagers need a high protein diet because they are still growing.

- ✓ in some countries people eat very little protein.

- ✓ we eat carbohydrates and fats to give us energy.

- ✓ enzymes help speed up the process of digestion where large, insoluble materials are broken down into small, soluble chemicals.

- ✓ the enzymes in the mouth are different to the enzymes in the stomach.

I can ...

- ✓ name foods rich in carbohydrates, proteins, fats, vitamins and minerals.

- ✓ interpret data on food labels.

- ✓ test food for starch
  ⮕ CAN-DO TASK Level ①.

- ✓ test food for glucose
  ⮕ CAN-DO TASK Level ②.

- ✓ record my daily protein intake
  ⮕ CAN-DO TASK Level ③.

- ✓ label a diagram of the digestive system.

Nutrition information

Typical values Per 100g: **Energy 1073 kJ, 253 kcal; Protein 0.5g; Carbohydrate** 62.4g of which **sugars 53.6g** of which starch trace; **Fat 0.1g** of which **saturates** trace; **Fibre 1.1g; Salt trace** of which sodium trace.

Typical values Per 15g serving: **Energy 161 kJ 38 kcal; Protein 0.1g; Carbohydrate 9.4g,** of which **sugars** 8.0g of which starch trace; **Fat trace** of which **saturates trace; Fibre 0.2g; Salt** trace of which sodium trace.

Control systems

I am a district nurse

My job is all about helping people in their own homes.

I spend time with people who have diabetes. I help them understand how to control their blood sugar. I also spend time with elderly people giving them advice about things like how to keep warm.

In my job, I need to know how the body keeps at the right temperature, how the kidneys make urine and how blood sugar is controlled.

Staying in balance

Explorers in the desert have to cope with temperatures above 40 °C. It may be hot on the outside but the body temperature stays at about 37 °C. If the body temperature changes too much, cells in the body are damaged.

It is the same for the amount of water and sugar in our blood. The body works hard to keep these constant.

The outside environment is always changing but our internal environment stays the same.

Which do you think is hotter, the outside environment or the man's internal environment?

← Body temperature →

45 °C	40 °C	39 °C	38 °C	37 °C	36 °C	35 °C	25 °C	20 °C
You are dead.	You pass out. You are in a very dangerous condition.	You feel very hot. You talk nonsense and see and hear things that are not there. You will probably be sick.	You feel hot and sweat. You may be irritable.	Normal temperature. You feel warm and comfortable.	You feel cold and shiver.	Shivering stops – but you become very confused and sleepy.	You are in a coma. Your breathing and pulse are very low. Heart attacks can occur.	You are dead.

? QUESTIONS

1 What is normal body temperature?

2 Why is it important to keep our internal environment the same?

3 At what temperature might you pass out?

CHALLENGE QUESTION:

4 Sweating too much is bad for the body. Find out why.

key words: internal environment   sweat   temperature

Keeping warm

Your body works best at 37 °C. When you go into a cold environment your body loses heat.

If you get too cold you could get hypothermia. This means that your internal body temperature is too low. You start to feel sleepy and can pass out. If you get too cold you could slip into a coma and even die.

To stop this happening your body will try to keep warm by shivering. This is when your muscles contract and relax to create heat.

Your clothes and body fat help keep you warm and moving also helps.

Hot   Cold

Blood flows to the skin's surface so it cools down in the air. You look redder.

The blood flow to the ears and nose is reduced to cut down heat loss.

Muscles shiver to create heat.

Sweat is released. It takes heat from you when it evaporates.

Most blood keeps away from the skin to reduce heat loss. You look paler.

Hairs lie flat so less air is trapped.

Hairs stand on end to trap warm air.

How the body tries to control its internal temperature.

Why is it important to keep warm?

CAN-DO TASK
Level 3 **2** 1

I can make a leaflet to warn old people about the dangers of hypothermia.

Hypothermia and the elderly

To keep warm when it is cold we can move around. Muscles create heat when they move the body. Some old people find it hard to move. This means they may spend all day sitting in a chair. In the winter if they don't keep their house warm they could get hypothermia.

? QUESTIONS

5 What is hypothermia?

6 Write down **three** things your body does to keep you warm in the cold.

7 Write down **three** things your body does to keep you cool when it is hot.

CHALLENGE QUESTION:

8 Why is an older person more likely to get hypothermia?

key words: blood flow   coma   hypothermia   shiver   sweat

Water in and water out

70% of our body is made of water. It is important that we get enough to drink. Water is needed to make blood and digestive juices. Chemical reactions in our body need water.

The kidneys

The kidneys control the amount of water in our body.

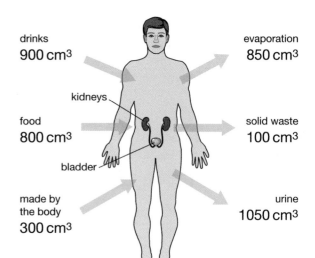

In   **Out**

drinks
900 cm³

kidneys

food
800 cm³

bladder

made by the body
300 cm³

evaporation
850 cm³

solid waste
100 cm³

urine
1050 cm³

How we lose and gain water each day.

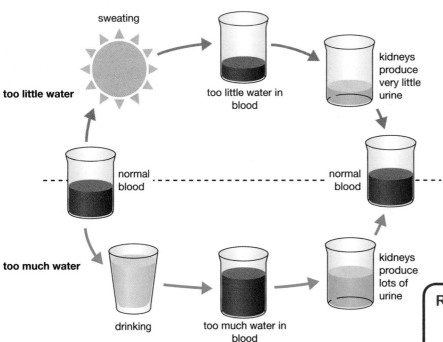

sweating

too little water

too little water in blood

kidneys produce very little urine

normal blood

normal blood

too much water

drinking

too much water in blood

kidneys produce lots of urine

How the kidneys control the amount of water in our blood.

Remember, the kidneys make urine; urea is made in the liver. ⚠️

? QUESTIONS

9 Look at the diagram of how we lose and gain water.

   a) How much water do we take in our food?

   b) Calculate how much water we lose each day.

10 Which organ controls the amount of water in the body?

CHALLENGE QUESTION:

11 You drink the same amount of water each day. Will you make more urine on a hot day or a cold day? Explain your answer.

---

key words: kidney   urine   water

Sugar in the blood

A lot of food we eat contains sugar. When the sugar leaves the digestive system, it enters the blood. We use some of the sugar for energy. The extra sugar is removed from the blood and stored.

The pancreas

An organ in the body called the pancreas controls your blood sugar levels. When there is too much sugar in the blood, the pancreas makes insulin. Insulin makes the liver take the sugar out of the blood and store it.

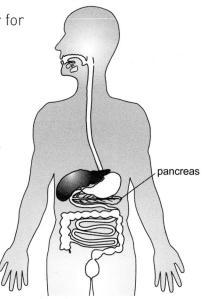

The pancreas helps to keep sugar levels in the blood constant.

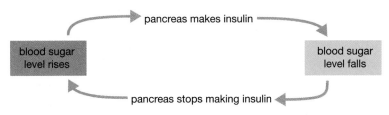

How sugar levels in the blood are controlled by the pancreas.

Diabetes

People with diabetes cannot control the amount of sugar in the blood. Halle Berry is a famous actor. She has diabetes.

To stay healthy people with diabetes need to be careful about what they eat. They may also need injections of insulin every day to control the level of sugar in their blood.

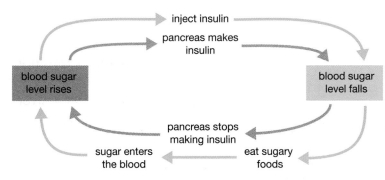

How a person with diabetes controls their blood sugar levels.

❓ QUESTIONS

12 Which organ makes insulin?

13 What does the body need sugar for?

CHALLENGE QUESTION:

14 Someone with diabetes has to be careful what they eat. Write down **three** foods they might have to avoid.

key words: blood   insulin   liver   pancreas   sugar

PATTERNS IN DATA
Keeping warm

Penguins spend a lot of time standing around in very cold temperatures. They huddle together in a large group. Every few minutes the penguins on the outside of the group move to the inside.

Darrel investigates how staying in a group can keep you warmer.

This is his plan.

- ◆ Put seven test tubes in a beaker.
- ◆ Put another test tube into a test-tube rack.
- ◆ Add the same amount of hot water to each test tube.

Record the temperature of the water in one test tube from the beaker and the single test tube. Record the results in a table.

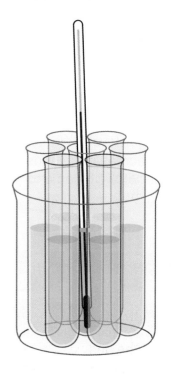

Time in minutes	Temperature of water in °C	
	test tube in group	single test tube
0	80	80
2	75	68
4	63	54
6	50	43
8	47	34
10	43	20

YOUR TASK

1 Draw a line graph of the data. Make sure:

- you label the axes
- use a suitable scale
- plot the results for the group of test tubes
- draw a curve through the points
- do the same for the single test tube so you have two curves on your graph.

2 Describe how the temperature changes between 0 and 10 minutes.

3 Which test tube cooled the fastest?

4 Use the results to explain why penguins huddle together.

5 Penguins on the outside of the group move to the middle of the group. Explain why.

B6 CHECKLIST

I have learnt that ...

- ✓ when our surroundings change it can affect our body's internal environment.

- ✓ the body's temperature is about 37 °C.

- ✓ the body loses heat in cold air.

- ✓ shivering and working muscles produce heat.

- ✓ stored fat, clothing and hair keeps us warm.

- ✓ sweating and more blood flow near the skin can cool us down.

- ✓ the kidneys remove water from the body.

- ✓ the body controls the level of sugar in the blood with insulin.

- ✓ insulin is made in the pancreas.

- ✓ diabetes is a disorder where people cannot control their blood sugar level.

- ✓ diabetes can be managed by diet or using insulin.

I can ...

- ✓ interpret the results of simple cooling experiments.

- ✓ label the bladder and kidneys on a body diagram.

- ✓ label the pancreas on a body diagram.

- ✓ make a leaflet to warn old people about the dangers of hypothermia
  →CAN-DO TASK Level ②.

- ✓ use a thermometer to accurately measure temperature
  →CAN-DO TASK Level ③.

Gasping for breath

I am an asthma nurse

My job is to provide advice and support to people with asthma and their families. People can telephone my help line with any concerns they may have about asthma.

In my job, I need to know what causes asthma and the effect it has on the body. I have to explain to people how the lungs work and why smoking could cause problems to asthma sufferers.

Why do we need oxygen?

Our bodies need oxygen to keep us alive. You take in oxygen from the air when you breathe in. The glucose from food reacts with oxygen to provide energy. This process is called respiration and it takes place inside every living cell.

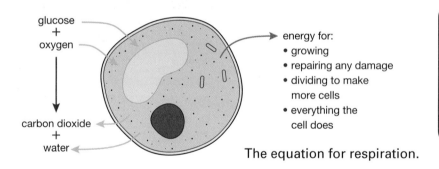

glucose + oxygen

carbon dioxide + water

energy for:
• growing
• repairing any damage
• dividing to make more cells
• everything the cell does

The equation for respiration.

> **Remember,** oxygen does not give us energy, glucose does. Oxygen is needed to release the energy from the glucose.

The water and carbon dioxide are waste products. You get rid of them when you breathe out. To see the moisture in your breath, breathe onto a mirror. You cannot see the carbon dioxide because it is a colourless gas. You can use limewater to test for carbon dioxide. The carbon dioxide turns the limewater cloudy.

? QUESTIONS

1 Which gas reacts with glucose during respiration?

2 What are the **two** waste products of respiration?

3 How can you test for carbon dioxide?

CHALLENGE QUESTION:

4 Cobalt chloride paper turns pink when it touches water. Describe how you could use cobalt chloride paper to show you breathe out water.

key words: breathing   carbon dioxide   oxygen   respiration

Inside the thorax

The upper part of the body is your thorax. The thorax houses your lungs. The volume of air you can hold in your lungs is called your lung capacity. An average man may have a lung capacity of 6 litres. A fit athlete could have a lung capacity of 7 litres. Someone who smokes may have a smaller lung capacity. The ribs protect the lungs and help with the process of breathing.

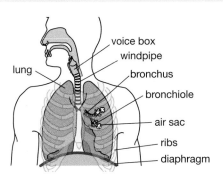

voice box
windpipe
lung
bronchus
bronchiole
air sac
ribs
diaphragm

The inside of the thorax.

Breathing in and out

Breathing involves moving air in and out of your lungs. To breathe in, the muscles on your ribs move your ribs upwards and outwards. When the muscles relax, your ribs move downwards and inwards. This forces the air out of your lungs.

Breathing in

Air is sucked into the lungs

Ribs pull the lungs upwards and outwards

Diaphragm pulls down

Breathing out

Air is squeezed out of the lungs

Ribs squeeze the lungs

Diaphragm relaxes

Exercise and breathing

Breathing rate gets faster when you exercise. This is because your muscles need more energy. Extra oxygen is needed to react with more glucose. This makes more carbon dioxide and water. Breathing quicker also helps remove the carbon dioxide from the body.

How the ribs move to get air in and out of the lungs.

Why do we sometimes get 'out of breath' when we exercise?

Remember, *breathing* is getting air in and out of the body. *Respiration* is releasing the energy from food. ⚠

CAN-DO TASK

Level   3   2   **1**

I can measure a person's breathing or pulse rate.

❓ QUESTIONS

5 Finish the sentences.

To breathe in, the muscles on your ribs move your ribs ...... and ....

When you breathe out, your ribs move ...... and ....

6 What happens to the air when it reaches the air sacs?

7 What is the name of the tube that carries air from your mouth to your lungs?

CHALLENGE QUESTION:

8 Plan an investigation to find out if boys and girls of the same age have the same lung capacity.

key words: lung capacity   lungs   ribs   thorax   windpipe

What is asthma?

Kerry has asthma. Asthma is a condition that causes the airways to narrow. This stops a person breathing in and out properly. The symptoms of asthma are coughing, wheezing and being short of breath.

The diagram shows the affect of asthma on the airways.

Asthma reduces:

◆ the speed that people can breathe in and out
◆ the lung capacity.

This is because the walls of the airways are swollen so the space for the air is smaller. The airways narrow further if the person exercises. Some people think that asthma is caused by pollution. However it has been difficult to prove if this is true.

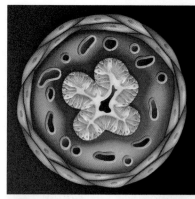

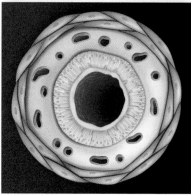

Which of these images shows airways from a person with asthma?

Inhalers

People with asthma may need to use an inhaler like the one in the picture. There are two types of inhaler – relievers and preventers. The doctor may also prescribe drugs that are protectors. They help to prevent another attack.

Type of inhaler	What does it do?
Reliever	Relieves the symptoms. Makes breathing easier.
Preventer	Reduces the inflammation in the airways. Helps to prevent an asthma attack.

How can an inhaler help a person with asthma?

❓ QUESTIONS

9 Describe what happens to the airways of people with asthma.

10 Write down the names of the **two** types of inhalers.

CHALLENGE QUESTION:

11 Design a poster for a sports centre which explains the symptoms of asthma.

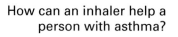

key words: airway asthma inhaler preventer reliever

Smoking

Smoking cigarettes can be harmful. Scientists have proven that certain chemicals in tobacco smoke cause cancer. Smoking can also cause heart disease.

Passive smoking

Smoking has been banned in public in the UK. This is to protect non-smokers. People who do not smoke may be passive smokers if they are near a smoker. Passive smoking is harmful too.

Children who live with smokers are more likely to have asthma. The table shows the chance of a child having asthma.

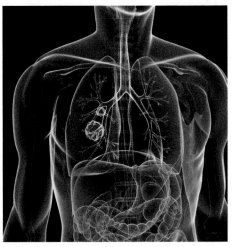

What health problems may be caused by cigarette smoke?

Year of study	Number of children in study	Chance of asthma in child of non-smoker	Chance of asthma in child of smoker
1986	8000	1	2.0
1990	770	1	1.1
1992	774	1	2.5

Tar – This clogs the lungs reducing their volume and the speed that people can breathe in and out. Colds, bronchitis and lung disease are more likely

Nicotine – An addictive drug that raises the heart rate. Nicotine patches are used to help people give up smoking

Hydrogen cyanide – A poisonous gas, used to execute condemned criminals in the USA

Solid particles – These are made of soot and many different chemicals

Carbon monoxide – A poisonous, odourless and colourless gas that stops red blood cells carrying oxygen

Some of the chemicals in cigarette smoke.

? QUESTIONS

12 Which chemical in cigarette smoke is addictive?

13 What effect does carbon monoxide have on the blood?

CHALLENGE QUESTION:

14 Explain how nicotine patches could help someone stop smoking.

---

key words: addictive   carbon monoxide   cigarette   nicotine   passive   tar

INTERPRETING THE DATA
Smoking and coughs

Some people think there is a link between people smoking and the health of their children.

The children will become passive smokers. They are at risk of getting the same lung diseases as smokers.

Look at the table. It shows the chance of a child developing a bad cough.

Cigarettes smoked by parent per day	Chance of child developing a bad cough			
	Sweden	Poland	Estonia	Mean of the three countries
0	1.0	1.0	1.0	1.0
1–9	0.7	1.4	1.8	1.3
9+	1.4	2.9	4.4	

YOUR TASK

1 Calculate the mean result for 9+ cigarettes.

2 Describe the pattern in the mean results.

3 Use ideas about cigarette smoke to explain the pattern.

4 What is surprising about the data from Sweden?

5 Produce a leaflet for parents explaining the dangers to their children if they smoke.

Maths Skills

Level **3** 2 1

Calculate arithmetical means.

B7 CHECKLIST

I have learnt that...

- ✓ breathing is caused by movement of the ribs.

- ✓ asthma makes the airways narrower.

- ✓ it is difficult to prove pollution causes asthma.

- ✓ breathing rate can be affected by smoking and asthma.

- ✓ smoking and passive smoking can cause heart disease and cancer.

- ✓ cigarette smoke contains carbon monoxide, nicotine, tar and solid particles.

- ✓ nicotine is addictive.

- ✓ respiration is when energy is released from food.

- ✓ respiration uses oxygen and glucose and makes carbon dioxide and water.

- ✓ during exercise muscles need more oxygen and glucose.

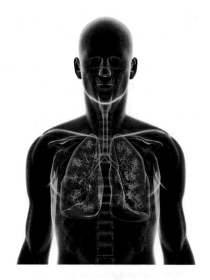

I can ...

- ✓ label the windpipe, lungs, and ribs on a diagram of the thorax.

- ✓ interpret data on asthma.

- ✓ interpret data on smoking and health.

- ✓ measure a person's breathing or pulse rate
  ➡CAN-DO TASK Level ①.

- ✓ test breath for carbon dioxide using limewater
  ➡CAN-DO TASK Level ②.

- ✓ test breath for water vapour using cobalt chloride paper.

Creepy crawlies

I am a park ranger

My job is to manage a large country park.

I work to conserve nature in the park. I also organise walks to show people what is living there.

In my job, I need to know what the animals and plants need to help them survive. I also check on the numbers of animals and plants, making sure the right plants are growing and removing any that are not wanted.

How do plants make food?

Look at the picture of giant sequoia trees. They can grow to over 80 m tall. To grow that tall they need lots of food.

Plants make their own food by photosynthesis. Photosynthesis takes place in the leaves. Carbon dioxide and water is turned into sugar. To do this plants need light energy from the Sun. Oxygen is also made as a waste product of photosynthesis and is released into the air.

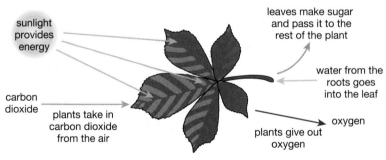

sunlight provides energy

leaves make sugar and pass it to the rest of the plant

water from the roots goes into the leaf

carbon dioxide

plants take in carbon dioxide from the air

oxygen

plants give out oxygen

The process of photosynthesis.

Why does a giant sequoia tree need a lot of food?

? QUESTIONS

1 Where does photosynthesis take place?

Choose from: flower leaf root

2 Which gas reacts with water during photosynthesis?

3 Where do plants get their water from?

CHALLENGE QUESTION:

4 If there were no plants, animals would die. Explain why.

key words: carbon dioxide light oxygen photosynthesis sugar

Predators and prey

Some animals eat plants; they are called herbivores.
Animals that eat other animals are called carnivores.
Carnivores that hunt for their food are called predators.
The animals they eat are called prey.

Tigers are predators which hunt and eat antelope.

Adapted to survive

Predators like tigers have adaptations to help them hunt
and kill their prey. The best adapted predators will get
more food.

The prey has adaptations to escape being eaten. The
animals with the best adaptations will be more likely to
survive.

> **Remember,** not
> all carnivores are
> predators. Some meat
> eaters just eat what
> the predators leave
> behind; they are called
> scavengers. ⚠

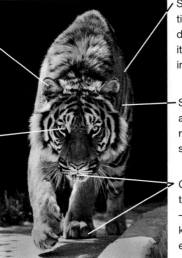

Tigers have very good hearing – to help with hunting

Good eyes at the front of the head help the tiger to see its prey

Stripes make the tiger more difficult to see as it stalks its prey in long grass

Strong muscles allow tigers to run fast for short distances

Claws and teeth – excellent killing equipment

Eyes on each side of head help the antelope see predators from all directions

Colour helps the antelope hide in the grass

Long legs to help the antelope to run fast

Some of the adaptations of predators and prey. Why are tigers
called predators and antelopes called prey?

? QUESTIONS

5 Finish the sentences.

Animals that eat meat are called ....

Animals that only eat plants are called ....

6 Why do tigers need sharp claws?

7 How does the colour of the antelope help it escape?

CHALLENGE QUESTION:

8 Tigers have eyes at the
front of their head.
Antelopes' eyes are on
the side. Explain why they
are in different places.

---

key words: adaptation   carnivore   herbivore   predator   prey

Food chains

Merlins are predators; they hunt small birds like stonechats. Stonechats feed on insects. The insects are herbivores; they feed on plants. Plants are producers; they use light energy to make food. Together the birds, insects and plants are part of a food chain.

plant → insects → stonechat → merlin

Food webs

Merlins are not the only animals to eat stonechats. Owls also eat them. This means that in any one place, there can be lots of different food chains. All the food chains make up a food web. Sometimes, one species in a food web changes; for example, its numbers go up or down. Other species are then affected.

The place where all the animals and plants live is called their habitat. There are lots of different habitats.

How do the Merlin's beak and claws show you it is a hunting bird?

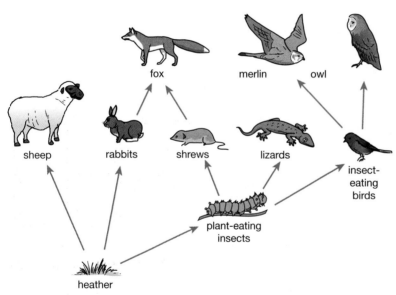

A food web for a habitat called heathland.

> **Remember,** in a food chain the arrow points at the animal that is doing the eating.
>
> lettuce → caterpillar
>
> The caterpillar eats the lettuce. Lettuce does not eat the caterpillar! ⚠

> **CAN-DO TASK**
>
> Level 3 2 **1**
>
> Given information I can match an animal to where it lives or when it lived.

❓ QUESTIONS

9 Why are plants called producers?

10 Mice eat blackberries. Owls eat mice. Draw a food chain to show this.

11 Look at the food web above. Write down the names of **two** herbivores in the food web.

CHALLENGE QUESTION:

12 Write down **one** example of a food chain from the heathland.

key words: food chain   food web   habitat   producer

Looking at habitats

Different habitats have different animals and plants living in them. Camels live in the desert but polar bears live in the Arctic. Each animal or plant is adapted to live in its habitat.

Scientists study different habitats to find out what is living there. To do this they use different sampling methods. Scientists also have to identify the plants and animals they find. They use special keys to help them do this.

Why is it important to return animals to their habitat after you have studied them?

Sampling methods

Sampling method	Used to …
net	catch flying insects
pitfall trap	catch animals crawling on the ground
pooter	suck up small insects
quadrat	count the different plants in a habitat

CAN-DO TASK

Level **3** 2 1

I can carry out a simple survey of a habitat.

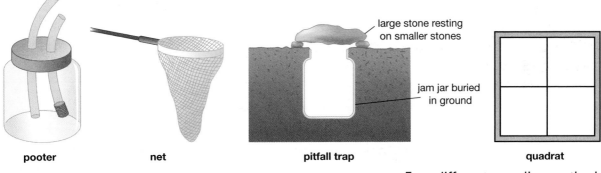

| pooter | net | pitfall trap | quadrat |

large stone resting on smaller stones

jam jar buried in ground

Four different sampling methods.

? QUESTIONS

13 Which sampling method is used to look for flying insects?

14 What are pitfall traps used for?

CHALLENGE QUESTION:

15 John uses a quadrat to count the number of dandelions in his garden.

His garden is 500 m². He finds three dandelions inside a 1 m² quadrat.

a) How many dandelions would this make in his garden?

b) Is this number accurate? Explain your answer.

key words: net   pitfall trap   pooter   quadrat

PROCESSING THE DATA

Shady areas

Rob and Cindy investigate the growth of algae on tree trunks. They predict that algae grows better on the north side of the tree.

To test their prediction they put a square sheet of plastic on the north side of a tree trunk. They record how much algae they can see through the plastic.

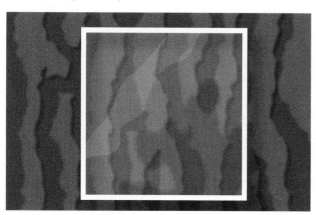

Rob and Cindy then do the same for all four sides of the tree. They then repeat this on nine other trees.

The table shows their results.

Percentage cover of algae (%)				
Tree	North side	East side	South side	West side
1	80	60	30	50
2	95	50	35	65
3	75	45	20	60
4	80	55	25	55
5	70	55	30	45
6	90	60	40	45
7	75	45	30	60
8	70	40	35	55
9	85	50	45	65
10	80	40	30	60
mean				

YOUR TASK

1 Calculate the means for each side of the tree.

2 Draw a bar graph to show the means for each side of the tree.

   Make sure:

   ● you label the axes

   ● use a suitable scale

   ● draw the bars at the correct height

   ● give your graph a title.

3 Which side has the highest mean?

4 Which side has the lowest mean?

5 Do the results match Rob and Cindy's prediction? Explain your answer.

Maths Skills

Level 3 2

Draw or complete bar charts.

B8 CHECKLIST

I have learnt that...

- ✓ plants need carbon dioxide and water and light to make food.

- ✓ photosynthesis is the process plants use to make food.

- ✓ oxygen is a waste product of photosynthesis.

- ✓ animals get their food from eating other animals and plants.

- ✓ some animals are adapted to be successful predators.

- ✓ some animals are adapted to survive being eaten by predators.

- ✓ animals that eat plants are called herbivores and animals that eat meat are called carnivores.

- ✓ if the number of one species in a food web changes it can affect the number of another species.

- ✓ a habitat is the place where an animal or plant lives.

- ✓ animals and plants are adapted to live in their habitats.

I can ...

- ✓ draw a food chain and interpret food webs.

- ✓ use a pooter, pitfall trap, net and quadrat.

- ✓ use a simple key to identify plants and animals.

- ✓ match an animal to where it lives or when it lived ➡CAN-DO TASK Level ①.

- ✓ carry out a simple survey of a habitat ➡CAN-DO TASK Level ③.

Fooling your senses

I am a special effects artist

My job is to make all the computer models needed in a movie. I create the explosions that can't be done for real.

I make computer images and models. These are then used to do things in movies that a human can't.

In my job, I need to know about how the human body reacts to sound and light. Knowing about the human senses helps me make the best special effects.

Eyes

Our eyes detect light and can let us see things. The light enters the eye and is focused on the retina by the lens.

Types of vision

Each of our eyes sees a slightly different image. The brain puts the images together so we can see in 3D. This is called binocular vision. If you close one eye you only have monocular vision. The image is still clear but it is difficult to judge distance.

Predators have eyes at the front of their heads. They have good binocular vision but a poor field of view. Prey have a larger field of view because their eyes are at the side.

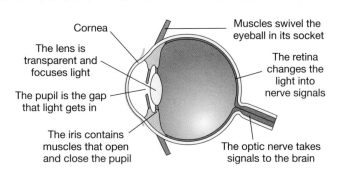

Cornea

The lens is transparent and focuses light

The pupil is the gap that light gets in

The iris contains muscles that open and close the pupil

Muscles swivel the eyeball in its socket

The retina changes the light into nerve signals

The optic nerve takes signals to the brain

The parts of the eye and what they do.

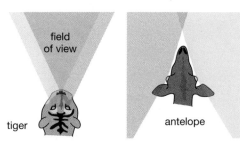

field of view

tiger

antelope

The different types of vision that predators and prey have.

? QUESTIONS

1 Match the part of the eye to its job.

lens	sensitive to light
retina	takes signals to brain
optic nerve	focuses the light

2 Write down **one** advantage and **one** disadvantage of binocular vision.

CHALLENGE QUESTION:

3 Explain why humans can see a 3D image.

key words: cornea   iris   lens   optic nerve   pupil   retina

Taste and smell

The durian fruit is supposed to have the best taste but the worst smell. It smells so bad that people are banned from eating it on trains in Singapore.

Taste and smell are closely connected. To decide on the flavour of food the body needs to taste and smell the food. Sometimes when you have a cold, you find it difficult to taste. This is because your nose cannot detect the chemicals in the food.

Why is durian banned in some places?

Taste and tongues

Your tongue has special cells called taste buds. Taste buds are sensitive to the different tastes of food. There are four main tastes we can sense:

- ◆ sweet
- ◆ sour
- ◆ bitter
- ◆ salt.

Different parts of the tongue are sensitive to the different tastes.

> **Remember,** taste and flavour are different – taste is what the tongue detects – flavour is the taste and the smell mixed together. ⚠

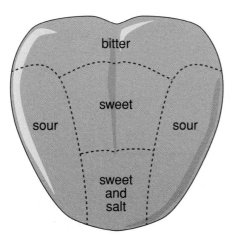

The tongue showing where the different taste buds are.

Why is it difficult to taste food when you have a cold?

? QUESTIONS

4 Where are taste buds found in your body?

5 Which part of the body is sensitive to smell?

6 Write down the four different types of taste.

CHALLENGE QUESTION:

7 Taste is detected by the tongue. Which **two** sense organs are needed for flavour?

key words: flavour   smell   taste   taste bud   tongue

Fast reactions

To be a good goal keeper you need fast reactions.

The reaction time is the time between a stimulus and your response. A stimulus is something you can detect, like sound or a moving object. The response is what you do.

Eyes, ears and taste buds contain receptors. Receptors detect the stimulus. Muscles are effectors as they move your body in response to the stimulus.

Why do goal keepers need fast reactions?

Reflex

Your body protects itself using reflexes. Reflexes are automatic reactions. If we touch a hot object we will pull our hand away without thinking. The reaction is fast to stop us from getting a bad burn.

The way you jerk your knee when it is hit is also a reflex. When you move from a dark room into bright light your iris closes your pupil. This stops too much light getting into the eye and causing damage.

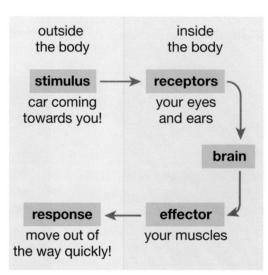

outside the body	inside the body
stimulus car coming towards you!	**receptors** your eyes and ears
	brain
response move out of the way quickly!	**effector** your muscles

Sequence of events showing reflexes.

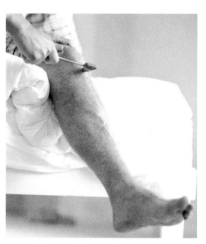

Which reflex is being tested?

CAN-DO TASK

Level **3** **2** **①**

I can measure the effect of caffeine on heart rate.

? QUESTIONS

8 Finish the sentences by choosing words from the list.

effectors   receptors   response   stimulus

When you touch a hot object the heat is the ....

The heat is detected by ....

Muscles move your hand away. The muscles are called ....

The movement away from the heat is called the ....

9 What type of stimulus does your ear detect?

10 Why does the iris make your pupil smaller in bright light?

CHALLENGE QUESTION:

11 Explain why reflexes need to be fast.

---

key words: effector   reaction   receptor   reflex   response   stimulus

Skin

Many people like to take good care of their skin.

Our skin protects us from the outside world. It contains millions of nerve cells called receptors. There are different types of skin receptors. They are sensitive to:

- ◆ touch
- ◆ pain
- ◆ temperature
- ◆ pressure.

Some receptors are deeper in the skin than others. The diagram shows that pressure receptors are deeper than pain receptors.

Why is it important to look after your skin?

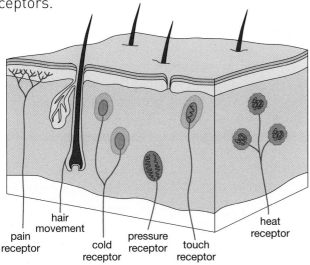

pain receptor · hair movement · cold receptor · pressure receptor · touch receptor · heat receptor

Cross-section of skin showing where different types of receptors are.

Sensitivity

Your fingertips are more sensitive than the back of your hand. This is because the receptors are much closer together in your finger tips. There are also many more of them.

The skin cannot detect actual temperature. It will only recognise a change in temperature. Try putting a cold hand in warm water. Your hand will feel very hot.

> **Remember,** receptors can be called other names like sensory cells or sensory nerves or nerve endings. They are all nerve cells in the body that detect stimuli.

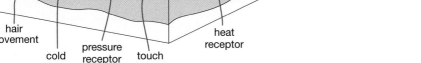

? QUESTIONS

12 Write down the types of receptors found in the skin.

13 Which type of receptors are found deeper in the skin?

CHALLENGE QUESTION:

14 Why is the back of your hand less sensitive than your finger tips?

key words: pain · pressure · receptor · skin · temperature · touch

REVIEWING THE METHOD
Sensitivity

Deion and Abir investigate how sensitive their skin is.

They predict that the fingertips are the most sensitive part of the body.

This is their method.

♦ Cut both ends of a straw to give two sharp points.
♦ Bend the straw in half. Put the points 1 cm apart.
♦ Blindfold your partner.
♦ Gently touch your partner's forearm with both points.

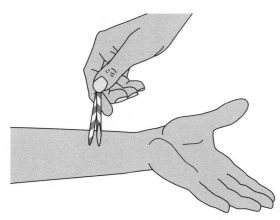

Trial	Number of points felt – forearm	Number of points felt – fingertips
1	2	2
2	1	2
3	2	2
4	1	1
5	1	2
mean	1.4	

♦ Ask your partner how many points they felt.
♦ Do the experiment again on the fingertips.

The table shows their results.

YOUR TASK

1 Calculate the mean for the fingertips.
2 Which part of the body was the most sensitive?
3 Explain why this part of the body is more sensitive.
4 Deion suggests they make a change to their method. When they touch the skin they could use one **or** two points.

Why would this change make their results more reliable?
5 Write down **two** other ways they could improve their method.

Maths Skills

Level ❸ 2 1

Calculate arithmetical means.

B9 CHECKLIST

I have learnt that...

⊘ binocular vision uses two eyes and monocular vision uses only one eye.

⊘ humans have good binocular vision but a poor field of view.

⊘ predators have eyes at the front of their heads and prey have eyes at the side.

⊘ 3D vision helps you to judge how far away something is.

⊘ there are taste buds on the tongue for salt, sweet, sour and bitter.

⊘ smell helps you taste the flavour of food.

⊘ a stimulus is a change in the environment.

⊘ receptors detect a stimulus and effectors respond to a stimulus.

⊘ reflex actions protect us from harm.

⊘ some parts of the skin contain more receptors than others.

I can ...

⊘ label a diagram of the eye and say what the job of each part is.

⊘ label a tongue diagram to show the different areas of taste.

⊘ measure the effect of caffeine on heart rate ➡ CAN-DO TASK Level ①.

⊘ interpret data on reaction times.

Food factory

I am a farmer

My job is to grow vegetables. I also keep goats for their milk. My farm is organic so I do not use any chemical fertilisers.

In my job, I need to know about different soil types. I need to know how to test the soil to find out what plants will grow best. I also need to know how to get the best milk from the goats.

Growing plants

There many ways to grow new plants from old ones. When seeds are given warmth, water and air they start to grow. This is called germination. The seeds grow into seedlings, which grow into a new plant.

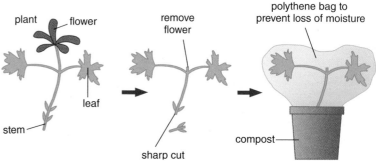

plant   flower

leaf

stem

remove flower

sharp cut

polythene bag to prevent loss of moisture

compost

Taking a cutting.

When a small piece of a stem called a cutting is taken and planted into soil, it can grow into a new plant. Strawberry plants grow stems called runners. Small plants on the runners grow into new plants. The part of the potato we eat is a tuber. Tubers left in the ground grow into new plants.

Cuttings, runners and tubers are examples of cloning. The new plants are identical to the parent plant they grew from. Plants grown from seeds come from two parents so they are not clones.

As plants grow they make sugar by photosynthesis. Some of the sugar is turned into starch. The starch is then stored for later use.

? QUESTIONS

1 Write down **four** different ways that new plants grow.

2 Finish the sentence.

Plants turn sugar into starch so it can be ....

CHALLENGE QUESTION:

3 Explain why plants grown from seeds are not clones.

key words: cloning   cutting   germinate   runner   seed   starch   sugar   tuber

Soil types

There are many different types of soil. Some soils are very dry and sandy. Others are full of clay and easily become waterlogged.

Different soils are good for growing different plants. Carrots grow in sandy soil but not in clay soil. Cabbages grow in clay soil but they are difficult to grow in sandy soil.

Soil can also be acidic, neutral or alkaline. Few plants will grow in acidic soils. Most prefer a neutral soil.

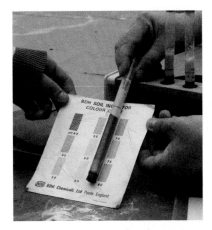

Why do farmers need to know the pH of their soil?

Testing soil

Farmers need to know if the soil is acidic or not. They can measure the pH of the soil.

- ◆ Put a spatula of soil into a test tube.
- ◆ Add a spatula of barium sulfate powder.
- ◆ Add 10 cm³ of distilled water.
- ◆ Add two drops of universal indicator solution.
- ◆ Shake the test tube then leave it to stand.

After a few minutes the soil settles. The colour of the universal indicator can be matched to a pH chart.

Soil can also be tested using an electronic pH probe. If the soil is too acidic, lime is added. This neutralises the acid.

Univeral indicator colour	pH	Soil type – acidic or alkaline	Plants that grow
red	1	very acidic	nothing grows
	2		
reddish orange	3	medium acidic	blueberries, heather
	4		
yellowish orange	5	slightly acidic	peanuts, potatoes
	6		
yellow	7	neutral	plums
green	8	slightly alkaline	cabbages, gooseberries
	9		
blue	10	medium alkaline	nothing grows
	11		
violet	12	very alkaline	nothing grows
	13		
	14		

The table shows the pH of some soils and the plants that grow in the soils.

4 Which type of soil holds more water: clay or sandy?

5 What is the pH of a neutral soil?

6 What could a farmer grow if their soil was pH3?

CHALLENGE QUESTION:

7 A farmer has sandy soil with a pH of 7. It is difficult to grow cabbages in this soil. Explain why.

key words: acidic   alkaline   neutral   pH   soil   universal indicator solution

Manure

Farmers can put manure on their fields as fertiliser. Manure is the waste that comes from animals.

When spread on the ground manure breaks down to release minerals. The plants then use the minerals to help them grow. Farmers have to replace the minerals the plants use.

Chemical fertilisers

Some farmers use artificially made fertilisers to replace the minerals. These are powders made in factories. Most chemical fertilisers contain the three minerals in the table.

Why do some farmers use manure?

Mineral in fertiliser	Use in plant
nitrogen	improves growth of plant, particularly the leaves
potassium	improves growth of fruit and flowers
phosphorus	essential for good root growth

Organic farmers

Organic farmers do not use artificial fertilisers. They make sure there are minerals in the soil by:

♦ adding manure
♦ growing different crops in the field each year, a method called crop rotation.

Opinion or fact

People have different ideas about organic food. Some ideas are actual facts; others are just their own opinion. That organic food tastes better may be just their opinion. However it is a fact that organic food has no artificial chemicals in.

Why do some farmers use artificial fertilisers?

Remember, plants do not get food from the soil, they get minerals.

? QUESTIONS

8 Which mineral helps plant leaves to grow?

9 How do organic farmers make sure there are minerals in the soil?

CHALLENGE QUESTION:

10 Are these statements fact or opinion?
a) Organic food costs more to buy.
b) Organic carrots look nicer than ones grown with chemicals.

key words: crop rotation   fertiliser   manure   organic

Where does milk come from?

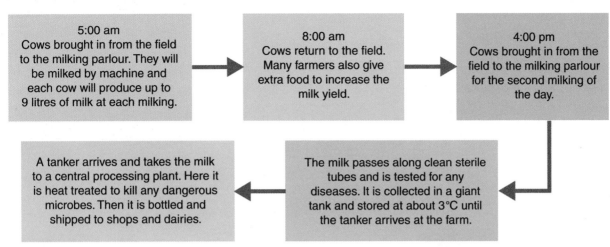

5:00 am Cows brought in from the field to the milking parlour. They will be milked by machine and each cow will produce up to 9 litres of milk at each milking.	**8:00 am** Cows return to the field. Many farmers also give extra food to increase the milk yield.	**4:00 pm** Cows brought in from the field to the milking parlour for the second milking of the day.

A tanker arrives and takes the milk to a central processing plant. Here it is heat treated to kill any dangerous microbes. Then it is bottled and shipped to shops and dairies.

The milk passes along clean sterile tubes and is tested for any diseases. It is collected in a giant tank and stored at about 3°C until the tanker arrives at the farm.

Safe milk

Milk is tested before it is bottled to make sure it is safe to drink. Milk can be sterilised or pasteurised.

♦ To sterilise milk, the milk is bottled. Then it is heated to 120°C for 20 minutes.

♦ To pasteurise milk it is heated to just over 70°C for a few seconds. The milk is then bottled.

Sterilising milk kills all the microbes in it. Pasteurising the milk only kills the dangerous microbes. The microbes left can make the milk go sour but they are not harmful.

Pasteurised milk tastes different from sterilised milk.

Why do some farmers feed their milking cows extra food?

Selective breeding

Milk can come from cows, sheep and goats. To get the highest yield from their animals, farmers use selective breeding. A farmer chooses the cow that gives the most milk. This cow is used to breed more cows. This way the farmer hopes to get the best offspring.

Why would a farmer selectively breed goats?

? QUESTIONS

11 How many times each day are cows milked?

12 Why is milk heated in the processing plant?

13 Describe how cows can be selectively bred to make a higher milk yield.

CHALLENGE QUESTION:

14 Explain the difference between pasteurisation and sterilisation of milk.

key words: pasteurise   selective breeding   sterilise

PLANNING TO COLLECT DATA
Soil test

Soils can be acid, alkali or neutral. Different plants grow better in different types of soil. Blueberries like acid soils and cabbages like alkali soils.

Farmers will test their soil to find the pH. The pH tells them if their soil is acid, alkali or neutral.

Universal indicator solution can be used to test pH.

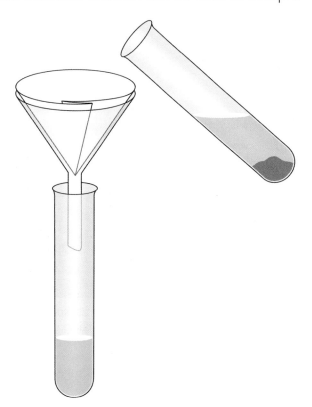

 YOUR TASK

Write a plan to find the pH of different soil samples. Read the information and use it to help you write the plan.

1 What apparatus will you use?

2 How will you make this a fair test?

3 What will you measure to get your results?

4 How will you make sure your experiment is safe?

5 Write out your plan as a step-by-step list.

B10 CHECKLIST

I have learnt that...

- ✓ plants make sugar and store starch.

- ✓ cuttings, runners and tubers will grow plants that are clones.

- ✓ clones are identical to each other.

- ✓ seeds need warmth, air and water to germinate.

- ✓ plants grow in different types of soil.

- ✓ fertilisers have chemicals in them to help the plants grow.

- ✓ plants need nitrogen, phosphorous and potassium for good growth.

- ✓ organic farmers use manure instead of chemical fertilisers.

- ✓ milk comes from cows, goats or sheep.

- ✓ milk is pasteurised or sterilised to kill harmful microorganisms.

I can ...

- ✓ grow plants from seeds, cuttings, runners and tubers.

- ✓ test the pH of soil.

- ✓ interpret data to find out which type of soil a plant likes to grow in.

- ✓ use universal indicator solution to find pH
  ⟹ CAN-DO TASK Level ②.

Drugs in society

I work as a pharmacist

My job is to measure out prescription drugs for people. I also give advice on which drugs to take and how to take them.

People come into my shop with prescriptions from the doctor. They may also ask me about symptoms they have.

In my job, I need to know about which drugs are only available on prescription. I also need to know about the affects of different types of drugs.

Prescription drugs

Drugs are chemicals that have an effect on the body or the mind. Some drugs help the body; others can be harmful.

Many drugs are only available on prescription. This means you need to get a doctor to prescribe them. If they are not used in the right way prescription drugs can be harmful.

Legal drugs

There are many drugs we can take without the need to go to the doctor.

♦ caffeine found in coffee, tea and some soft drinks
♦ aspirin and paracetamol
♦ alcohol
♦ nicotine in cigarettes and tobacco.

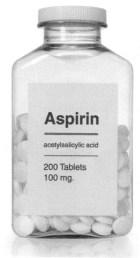

Aspirin

acetylsalicylic acid

200 Tablets
100 mg.

Do you need a prescription to get this drug?

? QUESTIONS

1 What is meant by the word 'drug'?

2 Write down the names of **three** different legal drugs.

CHALLENGE QUESTION:

3 You should not take drugs prescribed for somebody else. Explain why.

key words: alcohol aspirin caffeine drug nicotine prescription

Drug types

Drugs can change how you behave and feel. Different types of drugs have different effects.

The table shows the different groups of drugs.

Drug type	Effect on body	Examples
depressant	slows down the brain	alcohol, solvents
hallucinogen	changes what you see or hear	LSD
pain killer	stops nerve impulses so you don't feel pain	aspirin, paracetamol
performance enhancer	makes muscle grow	anabolic steroids
stimulant	makes your brain more active	nicotine, caffeine, ecstasy

Why are solvents harmful?

What does coffee do to a person's heart rate?

Some people find it hard to give up a drug they are taking. They have become addicted to the drug. Alcohol and nicotine are very addictive drugs.

Depressants can slow down a person's reactions. This is why a person should not drive after taking some drugs.

Caffeine and the heart

Caffeine is a stimulant; it makes the brain more active. This is why people drink coffee to stay awake. Caffeine also affects the heart rate. You can do a simple experiment to show this.

♦ Sit down and count your pulse for 30 seconds.

♦ Drink some coffee or cola.

♦ Count your pulse again – it should have gone up.

CAN-DO TASK

Level

3 2 **1**

I can measure the effect of caffeine on heart rate.

❓ QUESTIONS

4 Write down **one** example of a stimulant.

5 Which type of drugs stop nerve impulses?

6 Finish the sentence.

People find it hard to give up smoking because nicotine is ....

CHALLENGE QUESTION:

7 You are given two samples of cola. Only one has caffeine in it.

Plan an experiment to find out which one has caffeine in it.

key words: depressant   hallucinogen   pain killer   performance enhancer   stimulant

Illegal drugs

Drugs are classified by how dangerous they are.

The table shows the classification.

Class A	Class B	Class C
7 years in prison* and a fine for possession	5 years in prison* and a fine for possession	2 years in prison* and a fine for possession
life in prison for supplying	14 years in prison for supplying	14 years in prison for supplying
heroin, methadone, cocaine, ecstasy, LSD, magic mushrooms	amphetamines, barbiturates, cannabis	anabolic steroids, valium, temazepam

*This is the maximum prison sentence.

What is the maximum prison sentence for possessing cannabis?

Cannabis has changed from a class C drug to a class B drug. Some people would like to make cannabis legal. This is because some ill people find it helps stop pain.

Supply or personal use

Class A drugs are thought to be more dangerous than class C drugs. This is why possession of a class A drug may result in a longer prison sentence.

Only small amounts of drugs are needed for personal use. If a person is found with large amounts of drugs the police may think they intend to supply (sell or give) them to other people. This means the person could harm other people so the prison sentence is longer.

Suggest what this dog has been trained to find.

? QUESTIONS

8 Write down the name of **one** class A drug.

9 What is the maximum prison sentence for supplying LSD?

10 Why do some people want to make cannabis legal?

CHALLENGE QUESTION:

11 A prison sentence for supplying drugs is longer than for personal use.

Explain why.

key words: classification   possession   supplying

Alcohol

Drinking alcohol has effects that only last a short time. These short-term effects are:

♦ blurred vision
♦ slurred speech
♦ poor balance
♦ slower reactions.

Blurred vision and slow reactions would make it difficult to drive a car. This is why it is dangerous to drink and drive.

Alcohol use has long-term effects too. Someone who drinks for many years may have liver damage.

Alcohol kills more people than any other drug. It also causes people to break the law more often than other drugs.

Why do police check if someone has been drinking alcohol?

Remember, alcohol is just as dangerous to health as some illegal drugs. The fact that it is legal does not make it safe.

Testing drugs

Before a drug can be sold as a medicine it has to be tested. This is to make sure it is safe to use. There are some simple tests that can be done on drugs in the school laboratory. One test is to find out how soluble aspirin is.

To do this you could:

♦ Put 50 cm³ of water into a beaker.
♦ Crush up some aspirin tablets and weigh the powder.
♦ Add the powder to the water until no more dissolves.
♦ Weigh what is left to find out how much you used.

Do the experiment again with other types of aspirin.

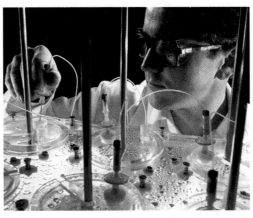

Why are drugs tested?

❓ QUESTIONS

12 Write down **three** short-term effects of alcohol.

13 What is a long-term effect of drinking alcohol?

14 Explain why it is dangerous to drink and drive.

CHALLENGE QUESTION:

15 Describe how you could test how soluble a drug is.

---

key words: alcohol   liver   long-term   short-term   soluble

INTERPRETING THE DATA

Drugs and reactions

Many computer games need fast reactions. Drugs can affect your reactions in different ways.

Some drugs speed up your reactions and others slow them down.

The affect of caffeine and alcohol were tested using a computer video game.

Look at the table. It shows the time taken to complete the game. The results are from the same person.

Drink given	Time to complete game in minutes
no drinks	7
black coffee	6
one pint of beer	8
two pints of beer	10

 YOUR TASK

Use the information to complete these tasks.

1 Draw a bar chart to show the results.

2 Describe the pattern in the results.

3 Which drug is found in coffee?

4 Use ideas about drugs to explain the pattern.

5 Produce a leaflet explaining the dangers of driving after drinking alcohol.

Maths Skills

Level **3** **2** 1

Extract and interpret information from charts, graphs and tables.

B11 CHECKLIST

I have learnt that...

⊘ drugs can help or harm you.

⊘ some drugs can only be got on prescription because they can harm you if used incorrectly.

⊘ drugs are chemicals that affect the mind or body.

⊘ caffeine, aspirin, paracetamol, alcohol and nicotine are legal dugs.

⊘ some people want to make cannabis legal.

⊘ nicotine is addictive.

⊘ drinking alcohol can make someone ill or commit a crime.

⊘ drinking alcohol makes you dizzy, slows your reactions and could damage your liver.

⊘ drugs can be classified depending on how dangerous they are.

⊘ it is dangerous to drive after drinking alcohol or taking some other drugs.

I can ...

⊘ test the solubility of aspirin.

⊘ name examples of different types of drugs.

⊘ describe the effects of stimulants, depressants, pain killers, hallucinogens and performance enhancers.

⊘ list the different classes of drugs.

⊘ measure the effect of caffeine on heart rate ➡CAN-DO TASK Level ①.

My genes

I am a forensic scientist

My job is to analyse DNA from a crime scene. I collect samples of blood, hair and saliva. I then take the DNA out from the cells. I use special equipment to make a 'fingerprint' of the DNA. This can then be matched to a suspect.

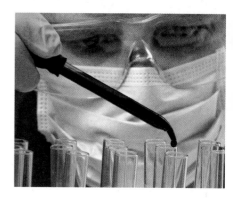

In my job, I need to know about genes and DNA. I also need to know about how DNA can affect how a person looks and that certain genes can be identified.

What are chromosomes?

Chromosomes are found in the nucleus of the cells in your body. They are made of a chemical called DNA. A small section of DNA is called a gene.

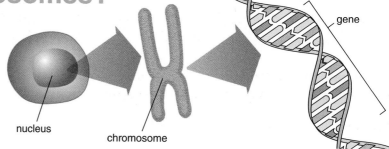

nucleus

chromosome

strand of DNA

gene

DNA in chromosomes is found in every cell in your body.

Everyone has their own set of genes. Your set of genes will be different to somebody else's. Everyone has their own unique genetic code. Only identical twins can have the same genetic code.

How many chromosomes?

Human body cells contain 46 chromosomes. They are matched into 23 pairs. One of the pairs is called the sex chromosomes. Females have two X-shaped sex chromosomes. Males have an X-shaped chromosome and a smaller chromosome called a Y chromosome.

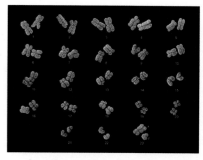

Are these the chromosomes from a male or a female?

? QUESTIONS

1 What chemical are chromosomes made from?

2 Which part of the cell contains the chromosomes?

CHALLENGE QUESTION:

3 How are the chromosomes of a male different to those of a female?

key words: chromosome   DNA   gene   nucleus

What do genes do?

There is a lot of variation in humans. This means we have slightly different features. Some of us have blue eyes and some of us have green eyes. People have brown eyes because one of the genes in their cells makes their eyes brown. They inherited the gene from their parents.

Can you spot any variation in these identical twins?

Genes and the environment

Genes control many features. Normally more than one gene is involved. People are different heights because lots of genes control their growth.

The environment also affects your height. You could have the genes to make you six foot tall. But you may have an illness that slows your growth.

Features can be controlled by genes or the environment or both. The table shows some examples.

Can you spot any features this brother and sister have in common?

Inherited in genes	Only environment	Both genes and the environment
tongue rolling	scars	hair colour
fixed or free ear lobes	accent you speak with	being good at sport

Remember, identical twins have the same genes, but the environment can make them look different. ⚠️

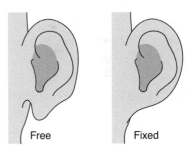

Free   Fixed

Fixed or free earlobes are due to inherited genes.

❓ QUESTIONS

4 Name **one** feature you can inherit.

5 Name **one** feature controlled by more than one gene.

6 Ben has blue eyes; he plays football for his school and speaks with a Liverpool accent.

Sort these features into those controlled by genes and those controlled by the environment.

CHALLENGE QUESTION:

7 Investigate variation in the members of your class.

Find out the colour of their eyes.

Draw a bar chart to show the numbers of people with each colour.

key words: environment   feature   gene   inherit   variation

How do genes control our features?

Family members can look similar or very different. This is because the genes we inherit may not show up. You could inherit a gene for blue eyes from your mother. But if you inherit a gene for brown eyes from your father, you have brown eyes. This is because brown is dominant over blue.

It is possible to predict your eye colour using a diagram called a Punnett square. Just follow the rules.

◆ Start with two genes from each parent.

◆ One gene could be dominant and will always show up.

◆ One gene could be recessive and will only show up if there is no dominant gene.

◆ One gene from each parent is passed on.

Can you have different eye colour to your parents?

The diagrams show two different examples. 'B' means the gene for brown eyes is dominant and 'b' means the gene for blue eyes is recessive.

Diagram 1 – The children will all have brown eyes because they all inherited the dominant brown gene.

Diagram 2 – One in four children have blue eyes. This is because they inherited only the recessive blue gene.

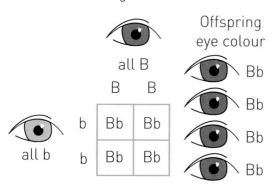

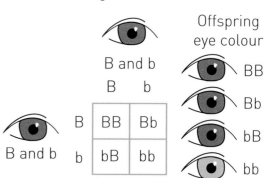

? QUESTIONS

8 Why is the gene for brown eyes called a dominant gene?

9 If both your parents have brown eyes can you have blue eyes?

10 Finish the Punnett square. What colour eyes do the children have?

	B	B
B	BB	
b		

CHALLENGE QUESTION:

11 Draw a Punnett square to show what happens if two people with blue eyes have children.

key words: dominant   Punnett square   recessive

Medical genetics

Some illnesses are caused by faulty genes. Cystic fibrosis is a disease caused by a mistake in just one gene. People with cystic fibrosis suffer from lots of lung infections.

Doctors can find out if a person has cystic fibrosis before they are born. Fluid can be taken from the womb during pregnancy. The fluid contains cells from the embryo.

The DNA in the cells can be looked at to find out if there are any mistakes. Many different genetic diseases can be found in this way.

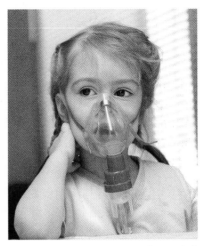

Can you catch cystic fibrosis?

Testing embryo DNA

The DNA of an embryo can be tested for more than just diseases. People could find out if it was a boy or girl. They could even find out the eye or hair colour.

People have lots of different ideas about testing embryo DNA. Here are just a few:

> I have a son with cystic fibrosis. I need to know if my next child will be the same.

> I don't want to know because I may think twice about having the baby.

> I think testing is dangerous. People could use it to have the perfect baby.

> My child is very ill. Testing an embryo could save their life. The embryo could donate some special cells to my child.

a

b

c

d

? QUESTIONS

12 Why is cystic fibrosis called a genetic disease?

13 How can doctors find out if a person has cystic fibrosis before they are born?

14 Which of the four people above agree with testing embryos?

CHALLENGE QUESTION:

15 Two people who do not have cystic fibrosis have a child with cystic fibrosis.

a) Is cystic fibrosis a dominant or recessive gene?

b) Draw a Punnett square to show what could have happened.

Use these letters – F = gene for no cystic fibrosis, f = gene for cystic fibrosis.

key words: embryo testing   faulty gene   genetic disease

PROCESSING THE DATA

Height and shoe size

Bill and Jenny investigate shoe size and height.

They predict that the taller you are, the bigger your shoe size will be.

To test their prediction they measure the height and shoe size of all the people in their class.

The table shows their results.

Height in cm	Shoe size	Height in cm	Shoe size
150	5	170	9
155	5	170	10
155	6	175	14
160	6	180	11
160	7	180	12
165	8	185	13

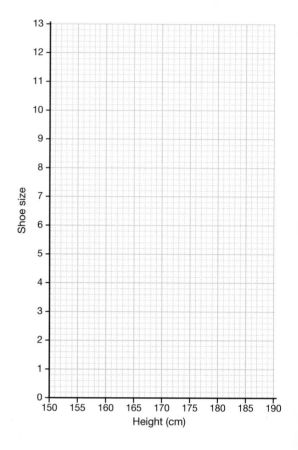

YOUR TASK

1 Draw a scatter graph to show the results.
Use the picture of the grid to help you:

- label the axes
- use a suitable scale
- write a title on your graph.

2 Describe the pattern in the results.

3 Which result looks odd?

4 Suggest a reason for the odd result.

5 Do the results match Bill and Jenny's prediction?

6 Write down one way they could improve their investigation.

CAN-DO TASK

Level   3   2   **①**

I can add results to a bar chart.

Maths Skills

Level   **❸**   2   1

Plot a simple line graph.

B12 CHECKLIST

I have learnt that...

✓ the nucleus of a cell contains chromosomes.

✓ chromosomes are made of DNA.

✓ DNA contains our genetic code.

✓ human features are controlled by genes and the environment.

✓ body cells contain 46 chromosomes.

✓ females have XX sex chromosomes.

✓ males have XY sex chromosomes.

✓ recessive genes can be hidden by dominant genes.

✓ some diseases are caused by faulty genes.

✓ embryo genes can be tested.

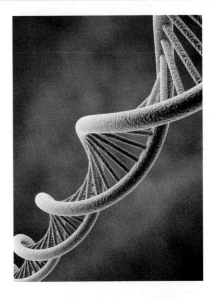

I can ...

✓ classify features into those controlled by genes, the environment or both.

✓ interpret data on human variation.

✓ use a Punnett square to show inheritance of features like eye colour.

✓ add results to a bar chart
➠ CAN-Do TASK Level ①.

Body wars

I am a scientist for a drug company

My job is to develop new vaccines. I make and test vaccines that can protect people from diseases.

In my job, I need to know how people catch diseases. I also need to know about the microbes that cause the disease and how people can be protected from them.

Microbes

Viruses
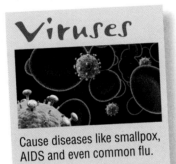
Cause diseases like smallpox, AIDS and even common flu.

Bacteria
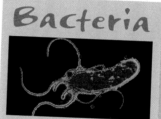
Important in the break down of waste materials. Cause diseases from sore throats through to some that kill in 24 hours!

Fungi
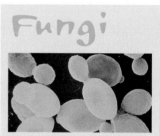
Include mushrooms that are big enough to see and tiny fungi too small to see without a microscope.

Microbes are tiny living things that can only be seen with a microscope. Most are made up of just one cell. Some microbes are useful but others cause us harm. The posters show the three main types.

Reproducing microbes

When microbes get inside the body they can reproduce very quickly. Our bodies provide them with warmth, water and food. These are the best conditions for microbes to reproduce.

Bacteria reproduce by splitting in half. Bacteria cells can double in number every 20 minutes. If you start with one cell, 20 minutes later there will be two cells. In two hours you can go from 1 to 64 cells.

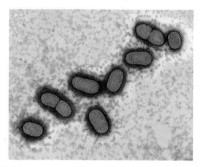
How many bacteria are about to reproduce?

? QUESTIONS

1 What are the **three** main types of microbe?

2 Write down **two** diseases caused by viruses.

CHALLENGE QUESTION:

3 You start with three bacteria. How many will you have one hour later?

key words: bacteria   fungus   microbe   virus

Avoiding infection

One of the easiest ways for microbes to get into our bodies is through our mouths. We can become infected by microbes on food. This can often happen if we don't wash our hands before eating.

Hygiene rules

It is important to stay healthy. There are different ways you can try to avoid infection. Here are some simple rules to follow:

- Always wash your hands after using the toilet.
- Always wash your hands before eating or preparing food.
- Keep raw meat below cooked meat in the fridge. This stops microbes on the raw meat getting onto the cooked meat.
- Cover salad when you put it in the fridge. This stops microbes getting on it.
- Make sure food is cooked properly to kill the microbes.
- Clean knives and chopping boards after use.

Why should you wash your hands before eating?

Remember, washing hands with water only will not kill all the bacteria. Using soap and water is better.

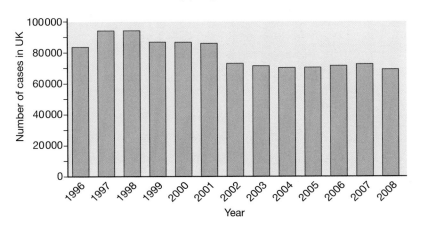

The bar chart shows the number of food poisoning cases in the UK. In which years were there over 90 000 cases?

Why is the way you store food in a fridge important?

CAN-DO TASK

Level 3 **2** 1

I can read data from a graph.

❓ QUESTIONS

4 Write down **two** rules about storing food in a fridge.

5 Why should you clean knives after you use them to cut meat?

6 Why should you cook food properly?

CHALLENGE QUESTION:

7 Draw a poster to show people how to reduce the risk of infection from food.

---

key words: hygiene   infection

Fighting infection

Your body protects itself against microbes in different ways.

If the microbes get past these defences the immune system takes over. The immune system makes:

- antibodies that destroy the microbes
- white blood cells that engulf the microbes.

Helping hand

Sometimes we need medicines to help us fight infection. Antibiotics are medicines that kill bacteria and fungi. They do not kill viruses.

We have to be careful when we use antibiotics. There are some bacteria that have developed resistance to antibiotics. These are not killed by the antibiotics and are called 'superbugs'.

We can prevent superbugs developing by:

- only using antibiotics when we need them
- always finishing the treatment – even if we feel better before all the tablets are used.

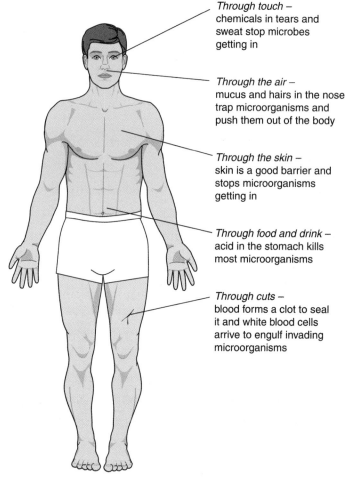

Through touch – chemicals in tears and sweat stop microbes getting in

Through the air – mucus and hairs in the nose trap microorganisms and push them out of the body

Through the skin – skin is a good barrier and stops microorganisms getting in

Through food and drink – acid in the stomach kills most microorganisms

Through cuts – blood forms a clot to seal it and white blood cells arrive to engulf invading microorganisms

How the body protects itself from microorganisms.

? QUESTIONS

8 What are **three** ways the body stops microbes getting in?

9 Name **two** ways the immune system fights infection.

10 How can we prevent 'superbugs' developing?

CHALLENGE QUESTION:

11 John has a virus infection. The doctor tells him antibiotics will not help.

Explain why.

key words: antibodies   antibiotics   engulf   white blood cells

Vaccination

Before you go abroad it is a good idea to find out if you need to be vaccinated against any diseases. The process of giving a vaccine is called vaccination.

We get vaccines against common diseases in this country. You may have had a vaccination to stop you getting measles or mumps. If you want to travel to other countries you may need different vaccinations. The table shows you what you will need for some countries.

Why might you need a vaccination before you go on holiday?

	India	China	Congo	Bahamas
Typhoid	R	R	R	(R)
Hepatitis A	R	R	R	R
Diphtheria	R	R	R	(R)
Yellow fever	(R)	(R)	C	R
Tuberculosis	N	R	N	(R)

R: usually recommended

(R): recommended if staying 4 weeks

C: compulsory – you cannot get in without a vaccination certificate

N: not needed

What are vaccines?

Vaccines contain a safe form of a microbe that causes the disease. The microbe cannot harm you but it makes your body immune. This means that your body can protect you from future infection from the same kind of microbe.

To vaccinate or not?

Vaccination has saved millions of lives. However there are some risks. Some people react to the vaccine and become ill.

In the UK some people believe their children have been damaged by a vaccine called MMR. The media have reported that MMR is dangerous. Their reports were based on an experiment that was proved wrong. But this worries parents and makes it very difficult for them to decide if their children should have the vaccination.

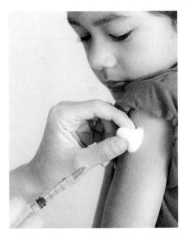

Would you take the risk of being vaccinated?

? QUESTIONS

12 What is a vaccine made of?

13 Which vaccines will you need if you go to India for one week?

14 Why do some people not want their children to have vaccines?

CHALLENGE QUESTION

15 The media can make it harder for people to make decisions about vaccination.

Explain why.

key words: immune   risk   vaccination

PATTERNS IN DATA
Bacterial growth

Every year drug companies test thousands of chemicals to see if they can kill microbes. They use plates of agar that have bacteria growing on them.

The chemicals are added to small wells in the agar plates. If the chemical works then the bacteria die leaving a space around the well.

The larger the space the better the chemical is at killing bacteria.

The table shows the results for five chemicals.

Chemical	Diameter of space in mm		
	test 1	test 2	mean
A	20	22	
B	2	4	
C	13	1	
D	14	12	
E	13	15	

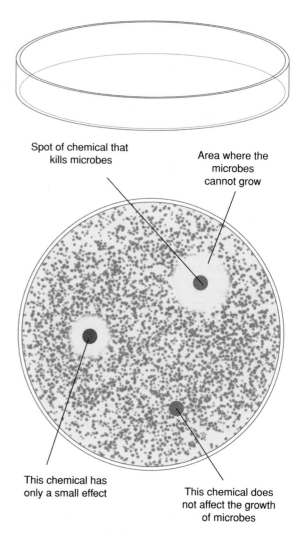

Spot of chemical that kills microbes

Area where the microbes cannot grow

This chemical has only a small effect

This chemical does not affect the growth of microbes

 YOUR TASK

1 Calculate the mean for each chemical.

2 Which chemical is the best at killing microbes?

3 Sort all the chemicals into order. Start with the one that kills bacteria the best.

4 The company decides not to use chemical B as an antibiotic. Explain why.

5 One of the results for chemical C may be wrong. How can the company find out which result is correct?

Maths Skills

Level **3** 2 1

Calculate arithmetical means.

B13 CHECKLIST

I have learnt that...

- ✓ microbes are bacteria, fungi and viruses.
- ✓ microbes reproduce quickly inside our bodies.
- ✓ white blood cells fight infection.
- ✓ food needs to be cooked and stored carefully.
- ✓ knives and chopping boards need to be cleaned after use.
- ✓ antibiotics kill bacteria and fungi but not viruses.
- ✓ some bacteria are not killed by antibiotics.
- ✓ vaccines make people immune to diseases.
- ✓ vaccines can be made from safe forms of microbes.
- ✓ some people are worried about giving their children vaccines in case the vaccines harm them.

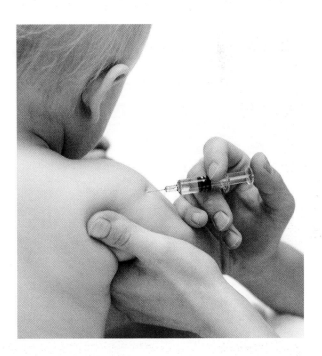

I can ...

- ✓ label a body to show how it stops microbes getting in.
- ✓ interpret data on the growth of microbes.
- ✓ explain ways people can reduce the risk of 'superbugs' developing.
- ✓ read data from a graph
  ➠CAN-DO TASK Level ②.

CHEMISTRY

Acids and alkalis

I am a textile technician

My job is to create new dyes for the fashion industry. I extract dyes from lots of different plants. I have to find ways to stick my new dye colours to many different fabrics. It is great when you get to see your work on the catwalk.

In my job, I need to understand about acids and alkalis and how they react. I need to understand how to use acids and alkalis to alter the colours of my new dyes.

1) Plant is ground up.

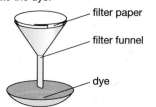

pestle and mortar

Extracting a dye

A dye is a chemical that can change the colour of fabrics.

2) The ground up plant material is heated in water and stirred to break down the plant further.

stirring rod
beaker
hot water
plant material
burner

Using dyes as indicators

Some dyes change their colour in acid and alkali solutions. We call these indicators.

The table shows some examples.

Dye	Colour in acid	Colour in alkali
beetroot	red	purple
red onion	red	green
geranium	orange-red	blue
litmus	red	blue

3) The mixture is poured through filter paper to separate the dye.

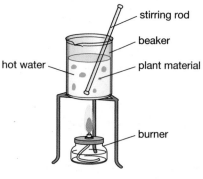

filter paper
filter funnel
dye

How to extract a dye from a plant.

? QUESTIONS

1 What is a dye?

2 Which indicators in the table turn red in acid?

CHALLENGE QUESTION:

3 Describe how you could extract the dye in rose petals.

key words: dye   filter funnel   filter paper   indicator   mortar   pestle

Strong acids

The acids used in science are mainly strong acids. They have a hazard label on them telling you they are harmful or corrosive. When you use them you need to wear safety glasses, and possibly gloves and a lab coat.

Natural acids

Many things we eat contain naturally occurring acids. Examples are lemons, limes, vinegar, tea and coffee.

These acids are weak acids and not harmful, so they do not need hazard labels on them. You do not need safety precautions to eat or drink them.

Acids have a sour taste and add to the flavour of food.

Hydrochloric acid is corrosive. What does 'corrosive' mean?

> **Remember,** not all acids are harmful. Many foods and sweets contain acids.

Alkalis

Alkalis are the opposite of acids. Sometimes they are known as 'antacids'. Alkalis are used to make oil into soap, to stick dyes to fabrics, to react with sand to make glass and to cure indigestion.

Single colour change indicators

Many indicators only show a single colour change in acids and alkalis. This means they cannot be used to find if a solution is neutral (not acid or alkali).

Indicator	Colour in acid	Colour in neutral	Colour in alkali
phenolphthalein	colourless	colourless	pink
methyl orange	red	yellow	yellow

Phenolphthalein only changes colour when a solution is alkaline, and methyl orange only changes colour when a solution is acidic.

? QUESTIONS

4 Give **three** examples of acids we eat.

5 Why should there be a hazard label on a bottle of hydrochloric acid?

6 Give **three** uses of alkalis.

7 What colour would phenolphthalein turn in acid?

CHALLENGE QUESTION:

8 Describe why we are not harmed by eating foods containing acids.

key words: alkali hazard label strong acid weak acid

Universal indicator

Solutions are not just acid or alkali. They can be strong or weak acids, neutral, or strong or weak alkalis.

Universal indicator solution is a mixture of different dyes. It changes colour depending on the pH.

The pH scale shows:

♦ Acids have pH numbers from 1 to 6.
♦ Neutral solutions are pH 7.
♦ Alkalis have pH numbers from 8 to 14.
♦ The stronger the acid, the smaller the pH number.
♦ The stronger the alkali, the bigger the pH number.

Remember, strong acids have low pH numbers.

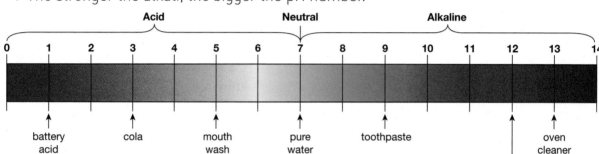

The pH scale.

Measuring pH accurately

Electronic meters can measure pH accurately.

Some pH meters are hand-held. They are useful for getting an accurate reading for a single solution. Some are connected to computers to monitor and record pH levels automatically. This is very useful in outdoor areas, like checking the pH of water in fish farms.

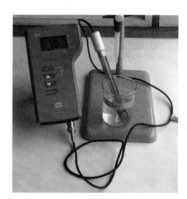

What does this pH meter measure?

? QUESTIONS

9 If universal indicator solution turns orange what is the pH?

10 What happens to the pH number as the strength of an acid increases?

11 What happens to the pH number as the strength of an alkali increases?

CHALLENGE QUESTION:

12 Suggest **two** uses of an automatic pH monitoring system.

key words: neutral   pH meter   pH scale   universal indicator

Neutralisation

When the correct amount of an acid and alkali are mixed, they cancel each other out. We call this neutralisation.

This reaction can be shown using the word equation:

acid + alkali → salt + water

Too much acid can damage plants. Farmers spread lime on their fields to neutralise acid soil. Lime is alkaline.

Your stomach contains hydrochloric acid. This helps break down your food. Too much acid in your stomach causes indigestion. Indigestion tablets contain a weak alkali to neutralise the excess acid.

> **Remember,** reactive metals react with acid to make hydrogen.

Acids and metals

Reactive metals like magnesium, zinc and iron react with acid to make hydrogen gas.

This reaction can be shown using the word equation:

acid + reactive metal → salt + hydrogen

You can show that the gas is hydrogen by holding a lighted splint over it; it burns with a squeaky 'pop'.

Acids and carbonates

All metal carbonates react with acid to make carbon dioxide gas. The reaction fizzes.

The test for carbon dioxide is to bubble it into limewater solution. The solution turns a milky white colour if carbon dioxide is present.

This reaction can be shown using the word equation:

acid + carbonate → salt + water + carbon dioxide

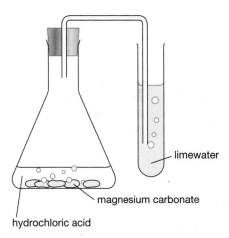

limewater

magnesium carbonate

hydrochloric acid

Reaction of a metal carbonate with acid.

> **CAN-DO TASK**
> Level 3 **2** 1
> ___
> I can carry out a test to show the presence of carbon dioxide.

? QUESTIONS

13 a) Which solution is used to test for carbon dioxide?

   b) What would you see in this test if carbon dioxide is present?

14 When a reactive metal reacts with an acid, what is made besides hydrogen?

CHALLENGE QUESTION:

15 Give **two** useful examples of neutralisation.

key words: carbon dioxide   hydrogen   limewater   neutralisation

PLANNING TO COLLECT DATA

Indigestion tablets

Many people get indigestion if they eat too much food, or eat too fast. Indigestion is a build up of acid in the stomach. The acid is there to help break down food and kill bacteria.

If you get indigestion, acid can bubble up into your oesophagus and burn it. We call this heartburn and it hurts. Indigestion can make you feel bloated or sick.

Indigestion tablets contain chemicals that neutralise the extra acid in your stomach.

If indigestion tablets are dissolved in water they make an alkali. Adding universal indicator solution shows this. Adding acid to the indigestion tablet neutralises it. This means the pH changes to 7.

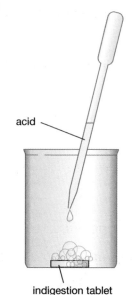

acid

indigestion tablet

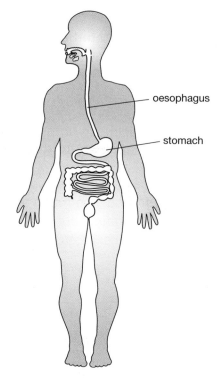

oesophagus

stomach

pH SCALE

| 1 | 2 | 3 | 4 | 5 | 6 | 7 | 8 | 9 | 10 | 11 | 12 | 13 | 14 |

YOUR TASK

Write a plan to find the amount of indigestion tablets needed to neutralise $10\,cm^3$ of acid. Read the information and use it to help you write your plan.

1 Indigestion tablets are different sizes and shapes. How will you make sure you use the same amounts?

2 What else do you need to do to make this a fair test?

3 What will you measure to get your results?

4 How will you know when the experiment has finished?

5 How will you make sure your experiment is safe?

6 Write out your plan as a step-by-step list.

CAN-DO TASK

Level 3 2 **1**

I can use a measuring cylinder to measure volume.

C1 CHECKLIST

I have learnt that ...

✓ lemons, limes and vinegar contain acids.

✓ the colour of some dyes can be changed by adding acid or alkali.

✓ alkalis are used to make soap, glass and chemicals for dyes.

✓ indicators can be used to classify acids, neutral and alkali solutions.

✓ universal indicator solution measures the pH and strength of solutions.

✓ pH can be measured electronically.

✓ acids fizz with carbonates to make carbon dioxide gas.

✓ magnesium, zinc and iron react with acid to make hydrogen.

✓ neutralisation happens when an acid and alkali react.

✓ neutralisation is used to cure indigestion and reduce soil acidity.

I can ...

✓ name basic laboratory equipment.

✓ use a measuring cylinder to measure volume
⟹CAN-DO TASK Level ①.

✓ carry out a test to show the presence of carbon dioxide
⟹CAN-DO TASK Level ②.

✓ test for hydrogen.

✓ use indicators to find if substances are acid or alkali.

✓ use universal indicator solution to find pH
⟹CAN-DO TASK Level ②.

✓ work safely with acids and alkalis.

Cooking and cleaning

I am a trainee chef

I work in a hotel kitchen. I have to show the Head Chef that I can cook many different dishes, using different methods. I use herbs and spices to flavour some dishes. I also learn about food safety and hygiene. I need to make sure my uniform is cleaned correctly.

In my job, I need to understand the chemical changes that happen when food is cooked and how chemicals like baking powder work. I also need to understand how cleaning products work.

Raw food

Some foods can be eaten raw. This means you do not need to cook them. Examples are fresh fruits, nuts and seeds, salad vegetables, and some fish dishes.

Is the fish in this sushi raw or cooked?

Cooked food

Food is cooked to improve its texture, taste and flavour. This makes it easier to chew and digest and kills any microbes in the food. Raw potatoes are hard, do not taste nice and can give you stomach ache. Cooking makes the potato softer so it is easier to digest and makes it taste better.

You can cook food in different ways. Potatoes can be:

♦ fried
♦ steamed
♦ baked in an oven
♦ boiled in water
♦ grilled
♦ microwaved.

The way you cook potatoes changes the way they taste. Fried chips taste very different to mashed potato.

? QUESTIONS

1 Name **two** foods that can be eaten raw.

2 Name **six** different ways to cook food.

3 Why does cooking change the taste of food?

CHALLENGE QUESTION:

4 Explain why food is cooked.

key words: flavour   raw food   taste   texture

Chemical changes

When food is cooked a chemical change takes place. Chemical changes make new substances. When meat is cooked the protein in it is changed forever. It cannot be changed back (reversed).

> **Remember,** a chemical change makes a new substance that cannot be changed back. ⚠️

Baking cakes

To make a sponge cake you need to weigh out and mix equal amounts of butter, sugar, eggs and self-raising flour.

- ◆ Mixing the ingredients traps air. This expands during cooking making the cake rise a little.
- ◆ Self-raising flour contains baking powder. This is a raising agent.
- ◆ When the cake mixture cooks in a hot oven, the baking powder releases carbon dioxide gas.
- ◆ The carbon dioxide gas forms bubbles that get trapped. This makes the cake rise even more.
- ◆ The cake hardens as it cooks, so it keeps its shape when it cools.

What makes cakes rise?

Fermentation

Fermentation is used to make bread, beer and wine. A useful microbe called yeast feeds on sugar, making alcohol and carbon dioxide gas.

When bread is cooked, the carbon dioxide makes the bread rise. Cooking kills the yeast and the alcohol that is made evaporates into the air.

To make beer or wine, sugar solution, yeast and flavouring are mixed in a container and left at room temperature for a few weeks.

? QUESTIONS

5 What does baking powder do?

6 What gas is released when baking powder is heated?

7 Why is bread not alcoholic?

CHALLENGE QUESTION:

8 Write a word equation for fermentation.

key words: baking powder   carbon dioxide   fermentation

Soap

Soap has been used since ancient times for washing and cleaning clothes.

You can make soap from a kit, but it is quite an expensive method. Soap is made when animal fat or plant oil is heated with an alkali.

In some places, the water supply has chemicals containing calcium dissolved in it. The water is described as hard. In hard water areas soap does not make a lather (form bubbles). If your kettle furs up with limescale you live in a hard water area.

Soap can also make a scum if it is used in hard water areas. In your bath, the scum sticks to the sides of the bath forming a white ring.

What is soap used for?

> **Remember,** in hard water areas soaps make scum, but detergents do not. ⚠️

Detergents

Detergents were invented in the 1920s, after the First World War. Detergents are made from crude oil. They are cheaper to make than soap. Detergents can be powders or liquids. They are used for washing clothes and cleaning surfaces. Detergents do not make scum in hard water areas.

How detergents work

1 Detergent particles have two different ends, a round-head and a thin tail. The round-head end is attracted to water.

2 The tails of the particles are attracted to the grease and stick in it.

3 The grease is surrounded by detergent particles and is lifted off the cloth.

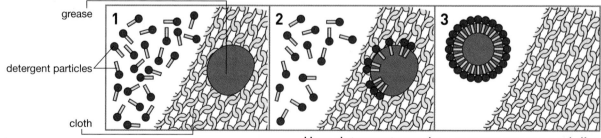

grease

detergent particles

cloth

How detergents work to remove grease and dirt.

❓ QUESTIONS

9 How is soap made?

10 Why does scum form in hard water areas?

CHALLENGE QUESTION:

11 When grease is removed by a detergent, why does it stay separated?

key words: animal fat   crude oil   detergent   plant oil   soap

Washing powders

Biological washing powders contain enzymes. Enzymes are protein molecules that speed up reactions without being used up. They are called biological catalysts.

In washing powders enzymes digest food stains. A different enzyme is needed for each type of food, so biological washing powders contain many different enzymes.

An enzyme works by being the right shape for the food molecule to fit in. This is known as the 'lock and key' model, as only the right shape food (key) fits into the enzyme (lock).

Biological washing powders work below 40 °C. Temperatures over 40 °C destroy enzymes. Some people get a rash if they wear clothes washed in biological washing powder because they are sensitive to one or more of the enzymes in the powder. They need to use a non-biological washing powder which does not contain enzymes.

> Remember, enzymes do not get used up; they keep working again and again.

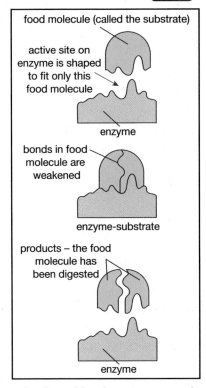

How 'lock and key' enzymes work.

Care labels

Most clothes have a care label explaining how to look after them.

Here are the main ones.

Care symbol	Meaning	Care symbol	Meaning
⬒ hand wash	hand wash only	◯	dry clean only
40	machine wash at 40 °C	⌧	do not tumble dry
⬙	do not bleach	⌂ iron	iron on low heat

? QUESTIONS

12 What helps to digest food in a biological washing powder?

13 a) What does an open circle mean on a wash label?

b) What is the symbol for iron on a low heat?

CHALLENGE QUESTION:

14 Describe how an enzyme in a biological washing powder helps to digest food.

key words: biological   catalyst   enzyme   molecule   non-biological

PLANNING TO COLLECT DATA

Heating baking powder

Baking powder is used to make cakes rise.

When baking powder is heated it gives out carbon dioxide gas. This gas pushes the dough apart.

If baking powder is heated using the equipment in the diagram, the carbon dioxide gas bubbles out of the tube.

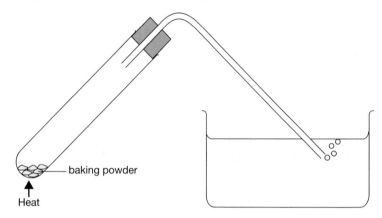

baking powder

Heat

If different amounts of baking powder are heated, different volumes of carbon dioxide gas are made.

 YOUR TASK

Write a plan to find out how much carbon dioxide gas is made when different amounts of baking powder are heated.

1 How many experiments will you need to do to get enough results to draw a graph?

2 How will you measure the different amounts of baking powder that you will heat?

3 Can you think of a way to collect and measure the carbon dioxide gas that is made?

4 What equipment will you need?

5 How will you make your practical task a fair test?

6 What will you do to make sure your experiment is safe?

7 Write or draw out your final plan as a step-by-step list.

C2 CHECKLIST

I have learnt that...

- ✓ some foods can be eaten raw.

- ✓ food can be cooked in different ways: boiling, frying, grilling, steaming and using a microwave or conventional oven.

- ✓ cooking changes the taste, flavour and texture of food.

- ✓ chemical changes make new substances and are irreversible.

- ✓ carbon dioxide is made when baking powder is heated and it is used to make cakes rise.

- ✓ yeast reacts with sugar to make alcohol and carbon dioxide.

- ✓ soap is made when an alkali reacts with fat or oil.

- ✓ detergents are made from crude oil.

- ✓ biological washing powders contain enzymes.

- ✓ care labels explain how to look after clothes.

I can ...

- ✓ plan to compare different amounts of baking powders.

- ✓ use diagrams to show how detergents work.

- ✓ interpret care labels.

Colours and smells

I am a paint research scientist

Many people think I just mix paints to make new colours. What my job is really about is making paints easier to use, with faster drying times and better finishes. I also try to reduce the smell when paint dries and make it easier to clean brushes and rollers after use.

In my job, I need to understand what different types of paint are used for, how solvents work and the effect of temperature on how much pigment dissolves and on drying times.

Using paint

Paint is used to decorate and protect our homes. Wood surfaces are protected using gloss paint. Inside walls are painted with emulsion paint.

Paint is also used to protect metals, like gates and railings. The Forth Railway Bridge in Scotland is so big it takes years to paint it. In the past, it was a never ending task. Recently, a special paint has been used that should last 30 years.

What is paint?

Paint contains three chemicals that are mixed together.
- ♦ The pigment gives the paint its colour.
- ♦ The binder sticks the paint to the surface.
- ♦ The solvent keeps the paint liquid and runny.

When the paint is used, the solvent evaporates and the paint dries on the surface.

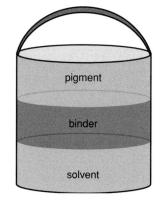

The chemical that make up paint.

? QUESTIONS

1 What does the pigment do in paint?

2 Which part of the paint sticks the paint to surfaces?

CHALLENGE QUESTION:

3 Describe the role of a solvent in paint.

---

key words: binder   paint   pigment   solvent

Paint for decorating your home

Gloss paint is used on wood and metal surfaces, both inside and outside. Gloss paint contains an oil-based solvent. This makes it waterproof when it dries, but also makes it expensive.

Oil-based paint dries slowly and has a strong smell that lasts a long time.

Emulsion paint is used on walls. It contains a water-based solvent that makes it useful for covering large areas, like walls and ceilings. It dries quickly as the water evaporates.

Paints for artists

Artists can use many different types of paint, for example oil paint and watercolour paint.

In oil paint the pigment and binder are dissolved in an oily solvent. When the paint dries, the solvent evaporates and the binder hardens. This forms a hard surface which protects the painting.

Watercolour paints contain pigments and a binder. Adding water dissolves the paint. When the water evaporates it sets.

What are the two main types of paint that are used by artists?

Special paints

Some paints change colour when the temperature changes.

They are called thermochromic paints.

They are often used to show if liquids are too hot, or are safe to drink, for example, in baby bottles and baby spoons.

Why is it important to test if food is too hot?

? QUESTIONS

4 What happens when emulsion paint dries?

5 What happens when oil paint dries?

6 Suggest why gloss paint is more expensive than emulsion paint.

7 Which paint would be best to cover a metal garage door?

CHALLENGE QUESTION:

8 Describe the difference between the way oil paint and watercolour paint dries.

---

key words: emulsion   gloss   thermochromic

Dissolving

Brushes and rollers used with emulsion paint can be cleaned using water. The emulsion paint dissolves in the water and is washed away. Emulsion paint is soluble in water.

The water is the solvent that does the dissolving.

If you try to clean a brush that has been used for oil paint with water, nothing happens. Oil is insoluble in water, so it does not dissolve. To dissolve oil you need to use a different solvent – one that will dissolve oil like white spirit.

Different solids need different solvents to dissolve them.

How can you clean oil paint off a brush?

Solutions

When a solvent dissolves a solid, it makes a solution.
A solution is a clear liquid, which means it has no bits in it.
Solutions can be coloured or colourless.

Dissolving at different temperatures

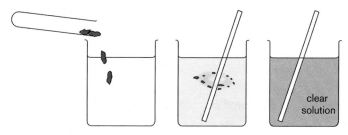

A coloured chemical being dissolved.

Most substances dissolve better at higher temperatures as shown in the graph.

Soluble substances like salt dissolve when water particles bash into the solid, breaking bits off. Heating the water makes the particles move faster, so they bash it more often and break up quicker.

CAN-DO TASK

Level 3 **2** 1

I can use a thermometer to measure temperature accurately.

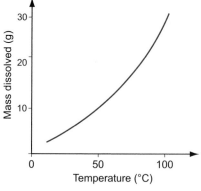

Graph to show the mass of a chemical dissolved with increasing temperature.

❓ QUESTIONS

9 What is a solvent?

10 What does the word 'insoluble' mean?

11 Why does hot water dissolve salt faster?

CHALLENGE QUESTION:

12 Use ideas about particles to suggest why some substances are insoluble in water.

key words: insoluble   particle   soluble   solution   solvent

Perfumes

Perfumes are substances that:

♦ smell nice

♦ evaporate off the skin into the air easily

♦ are not harmful

♦ do not irritate the skin.

To make a perfume, what will happen to this lavender after it's been harvested?

How natural perfumes are made

Many perfumes are made using scents from natural sources.

One example of perfume made from an animal is musk that comes from deer. To get the musk the deer must be killed.

An example of perfume made from plants is lavender oil. The lavender is harvested and heated with steam. Next the vapour is cooled to make lavender oil. This is called steam distillation. Rose oil is made from rose petals using steam distillation.

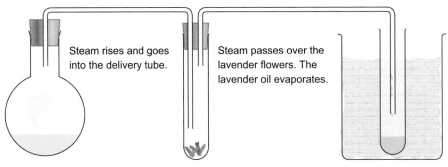

Steam rises and goes into the delivery tube.

Steam passes over the lavender flowers. The lavender oil evaporates.

The ice cools the lavender vapour. Drops of oil form on the delivery tube and collect on the bottom.

Steam distillation is used to separate the scented oil in lavender flowers.

How synthetic perfumes are made

Synthetic means made by humans. Fruity smelling chemicals called esters can be made by a chemical reaction using a weak acid and an alcohol. Mixing different esters makes cheaper synthetic perfumes.

Remember, all chemicals have to be tested to make sure they are safe to use. ⚠

? QUESTIONS

13 Why do perfumes need to evaporate easily?

14 Give **one** example of a natural perfume from:

a) an animal   b) a plant

15 What does 'synthetic' mean?

16 Describe how the scent from a perfume gets from your skin to your nose.

CHALLENGE QUESTIONS:

17 Name **two** chemicals needed to make a synthetic perfume.

key words: distillation   ester   evaporate   perfume   synthetic

INTERPRETING DATA

Using solvents

Kim and Ben's teacher gives them some information about the amount of different chemicals that can dissolve in water at 20°C and at 40°C.

The information is shown in the table.

Chemical	mass (g) dissolved at 20°C	mass (g) dissolved at 40°C
aluminium chloride	37	47
copper chloride	73	88
iron chloride	63	70
sodium chloride	36	37

Ben and Kim draw this chart to show the results.

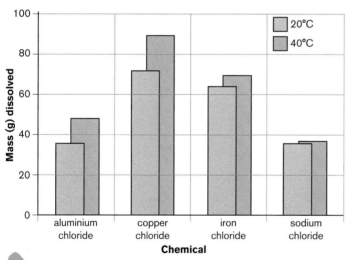

YOUR TASK

1 How much iron chloride dissolves at 20°C?

2 At 40°C, which chemical dissolved the most?

3 Which chemical showed the smallest difference in how much dissolves?

4 a) What pattern does the data show?

  b) Suggest a scientific reason for this.

Maths Skills

Level **3** **2** **①**

Select information from tables and charts.

Maths Skills

Level **3** **②** **1**

Read data from charts and graphs.

C3 CHECKLIST

I have learnt that...

- ✓ paints contains a solvent, pigment and binder.

- ✓ paints are used to decorate and protect and to create art.

- ✓ thermochromic paints change colour when they are heated or cooled.

- ✓ gloss paints use oil as the solvent.

- ✓ emulsion, watercolour and poster paints use water as the solvent.

- ✓ when a solid dissolves in a solvent, a solution is made.

- ✓ natural perfumes are made from plants and animals.

- ✓ perfumes can be made synthetically using a weak acid and an alcohol.

- ✓ perfumes have a pleasant smell and evaporate easily.

I can ...

- ✓ make a paint sample and show it works ➡ CAN-DO TASK Level ②.

- ✓ I can use a thermometer to measure temperature accurately ➡ CAN-DO TASK Level ②.

- ✓ interpret information given to me about what is in paint.

- ✓ understand the terms solvent, soluble and insoluble.

- ✓ interpret information about how much of a substance dissolves at different temperatures.

- ✓ understand why perfumes need to be tested.

Heavy metal?

I am a jewellery designer

I design jewellery for my clients. I use platinum, gold and silver metals together with precious stones like diamonds, rubies and sapphires. The designs are drawn on paper and the client selects the jewellery they want me to make. I also repair broken jewellery.

In my job, I need to know about how to shape and join different precious metals and how to fit precious stones. Sometimes I am asked to make less expensive jewellery. I can do this by electroplating (covering) cheaper metals with gold or silver.

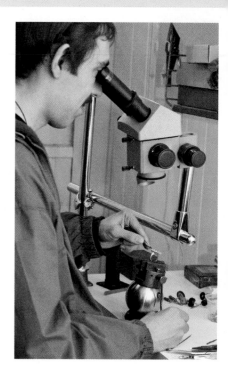

Precious metals

Gold, silver and platinum are very unreactive. This means they do not become dull easily. This is one reason they are used for making jewellery. Another reason is they can be shaped easily.

Because gold, silver and platinum are unreactive they are found as pure metals buried in the ground or on the bottom of rivers. These metals are quite rare. Some people spend their lives looking for them.

Gold, silver and platinum are shiny and heavy metals, so a small piece weighs a lot.

If you found a small 100 g piece of gold it would be worth around £3700, but prices change daily.

Each 1 kg gold bar is worth about £37 000. What are two bars worth?

? QUESTIONS

1 Name **two** places in nature where gold and silver are found.

2 Give **two** reasons why gold is used for making jewellery.

3 How much gold would £370 buy?

CHALLENGE QUESTION:

4 A gram of silver costs 54 p. What would a kilogram bar of silver cost?

key words: jewellery   precious   rare   unreactive

Electroplating

Some jewellery can be made from cheaper metals like steel or nickel and then coated with gold or silver to make it look more attractive and more expensive. Dipping the metal into molten silver or gold is one way of doing this, but it gives a thick uneven coating.

A better way is to used electroplating. This gives a thin and even coating. Electroplating uses an electric current. During electroplating, a metal dissolves and moves from the positive (+) electrode to the negative (-) electrode. The solution that conducts is called the electrolyte.

> **Remember**, during electroplating, new pure metal is deposited on the negative electrode. ⚠️

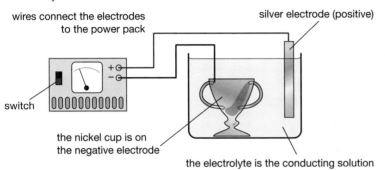

Electroplating. The silver electrode dissolves and moves through the solution to coat the nickel cup attached to the negative electrode.

What makes gold-plated cutlery strong?

Some people are allergic to metals, like nickel. If they touch nickel they get an itchy rash. Electroplating nickel with silver or gold stops the allergic reaction.

Expensive cutlery sets use steel electroplated with silver or gold. This makes cutlery look more attractive. Gold is quite soft, so having steel on the inside improves the cutlery strength.

Steel items can rust. To prevent this they can be electroplated with chrome to protect them. Chrome plating has a very shiny finish and is easy to clean.

❓ QUESTIONS

5 Give **two** ways to coat a ring with gold.

6 What is the purpose of the electrolyte in the diagram above?

7 Why is a gold-plated knife better than a knife made of pure gold?

CHALLENGE QUESTION:

8 Why is a thin, even coating of precious metal better than a thick, uneven layer?

key words: allergic   chrome   electrolyte   electroplating

Iron and aluminium

Iron and aluminium are cheaper than gold, silver and platinum. They are cheaper because there is more of them in the Earth.

Iron and aluminium ores are dug out of the ground. An ore contains a metal compound.

Properties of iron and aluminium

Aluminium is less dense than iron. This means the same volume of aluminium weighs less than iron.

Aluminium does not corrode, but iron does.

Aluminium is not magnetic, but iron is.

Why do you think aluminium was used to make these?

Making cars

Pure iron breaks easily. Adding small amounts of other substances to iron makes steel, which is very strong and hard. Steel is cheaper and stronger than aluminium so cars have steel frames.

Aluminium can be used for body panels and wheels to save weight and prevent rusting. Copper is used in electrical wiring. Lead is used in car batteries.

CAN-DO TASK
Level **3 2 ①**

I can identify some common metals: iron (using a magnet), copper, aluminium and lead (by sight and touch).

Rusting

When iron or steel corrodes we call it rusting. Iron rusts when water and oxygen come into contact with it.

Oxygen gas is in air, so when iron gets wet it starts to rust. Salt water speeds up rusting. If you live on the coast, the salt in sea spray makes iron objects rust faster.

Are cars made with one type of metal?

? QUESTIONS

9 Give **two** properties of aluminium.

10 Give **one** advantage and **one** disadvantage of using aluminium in a car.

11 Which **two** substances are needed for iron to rust?

CHALLENGE QUESTION:

12 Suggest why aluminium is more expensive than iron.

key words: corrode dense magnetic ores rusting

Copper metal

Copper is a metal and conducts electricity very well, so it is used in electrical cables. Copper ore is dug out of the ground. The main ore is called malachite. Its chemical name is copper carbonate.

The diagram shows how copper is extracted from its ore.

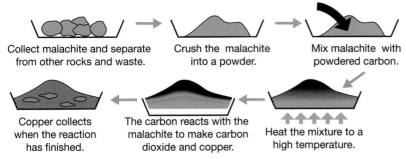

Collect malachite and separate from other rocks and waste.

Crush the malachite into a powder.

Mix malachite with powdered carbon.

Copper collects when the reaction has finished.

The carbon reacts with the malachite to make carbon dioxide and copper.

Heat the mixture to a high temperature.

How copper is extracted from its ore. Why is carbon added to the ore?

> **CAN-DO TASK**
> Level **3** 2 1
> I can extract a sample of copper from its ore.

Heating with carbon removes oxygen from the ore.

This is an example of a reduction reaction and can be shown by the equation:

copper oxide + carbon → copper + carbon monoxide

> **Remember,** reduction happens when oxygen is removed. ⚠

Recycling

All metals are a finite resource. This means they might be used up eventually so most are worth recycling. A problem is that metals are not always pure. For example, drink cans often have aluminium sides and steel tops and copper pipes are joined with solder containing tin.

Recycling is cheaper than getting a metal from an ore. It uses less energy and saves resources.

Metals like copper can be recycled by:
♦ collecting and melting down scrap
♦ using electricity to make very pure copper.

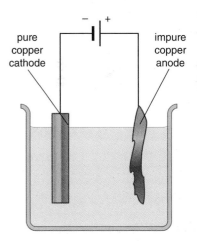

Using electricity to purify copper.

❓ QUESTIONS

13 Why does electrical wiring use copper metal?

14 What is reduction?

15 Which chemical is used to reduce copper oxide to copper?

16 What are the advantages of recycling metals?

CHALLENGE QUESTION:

17 Suggest a disadvantage of recycling copper pipes by melting scrap.

---

key words: electricity   finite   melting   recycling   reduction

PATTERNS IN THE DATA

Gina and Basmar investigate rusting.

They put nails into test tubes of water containing different percentages of salt.

They use this key to decide how much rust forms.

No rust	0
A bit of rust	1
Some rust	2
Lots of rust	3

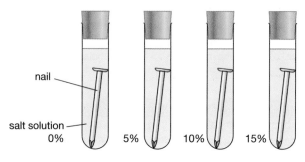

They check the results every day.

Here is what they find.

Salt %	Day 1	Day 2	Day 3	Day 4	Day 5
0	0	0	1	1	2
5	0	1	1	2	1
10	1	2	2	3	3
15	2	3	3	3	3

YOUR TASK

Use the results to answer these questions.

1 Which salt % rusted quickest?

2 How many tubes did not rust on day 1?

3 a) Do any of the results look like they might be wrong?

  b) Choose one and explain why you chose this result.

4 How long does it take for 15% salt to make lots of rust?

  ...... days

5 Which other salt % makes lots of rust?

6 What pattern is shown by the results?

Maths Skills

Level **3** **2** **①**

Select information from tables and charts.

Maths Skills

Level **3** **②** **1**

Extract and interpret data from tables.

C4 CHECKLIST

I have learnt that...

✓ gold, silver and platinum are found in the Earth as pure metals and are shiny and heavy metals.

✓ gold, silver and platinum are used to make jewellery because they are unreactive.

✓ some people are allergic to metals like nickel so this metal can be covered in gold to avoid this.

✓ covering one metal with another metal is best done by electroplating.

✓ electroplating allows cheaper jewellery to be made.

✓ rusting needs iron, water and oxygen.

✓ salty water speeds up rusting.

✓ copper is extracted by heating its ore with carbon and this is called reduction.

✓ recycling copper is cheaper than making it from its ore because it saves energy and resources.

✓ metals are a finite resource so are worth recycling.

I can ...

✓ set up equipment for electroplating.

✓ identify some common metals: iron (using a magnet), copper, aluminium and lead (by sight and touch)
➠ CAN-DO TASK Level ①.

✓ extract copper from copper ore
➠ CAN-DO TASK Level ③.

✓ describe an advantage and a disadvantage of using steel and aluminium in cars.

✓ interpret information about metals used to make cars.

✓ interpret information about recycling metals.

Fibres and fabrics

I am a safety clothing designer

My job is to design safety clothes. I make clothing for firefighters, ambulance crews and for the Army, Navy and Air Force. Clothes for rescue workers need to be brightly coloured, tough and waterproof. Clothes for the Army often need to be camouflaged so they cannot be seen easily.

In my job, I need to decide which fibres and fabrics to use to give the properties that are needed. I also need to make the clothes comfortable to wear, while still giving protection.

Fabrics

Clothes are made of fabrics. Fabrics are made by weaving or joining fibres together. Many different fabrics are used to make clothes. The fabrics used to make a garment are shown on its care label.

Natural fibres come from living things. Cotton comes from a plant, wool from sheep or goats and silk from an insect called a silk worm. Natural wool contains lanolin oil making it waterproof, but this is washed out when it is cleaned and made into fabrics.

Synthetic fibres are made by chemical reactions. This means they are man-made. Some man-made materials have replaced natural fabrics. Nylon is a lightweight and tough material. It has replaced cotton for making tents, sails and outdoor clothes. Polyester and polythene are also man-made.

> **Remember**, synthetic fibres are made by chemical reactions. ⚠️

How is raw cotton from plants made into cotton fibres?

? QUESTIONS

1 How is a fabric made?

2 Name a natural fibre from a plant.

3 Why is nylon a better material than cotton for making a tent?

CHALLENGE QUESTION:

4 Suggest some properties that a sail for a windsurfer should have.

key words: fabrics   fibres   natural   synthetic

Stretching fibres

T-shirts need to be made from fibres that stretch a bit so you can get them over your head. If fabrics stretch too much they lose their shape. Fibres also need to be strong and flexible so when clothing is folded, crunched up or washed, the fibres do not snap.

Fibres can be tested to find how strong or stretchy they are. One way to do this is to add weights to threads. When threads are made, they are not always exactly the same, so different bits of thread might give different strength results.

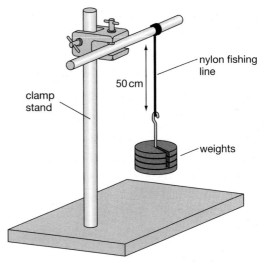

Apparatus to measure how stretchy and strong fibres are.

Waterproof fabrics

Many people who work outdoors need waterproof clothing.

Firefighters and mountaineers need to keep dry to stay warm and comfortable.

Scuba divers can keep warm and dry by wearing a dry suit. Dry suits have a tough waterproof outer shell with waterproof neck and wrist seals. The suit is filled with air to insulate the diver from the cold seawater.

Breathable fabrics

Waterproof fabrics keep water out, but also keep sweat in. Waterproof clothing can be improved by adding a breathable layer like Gore-Tex®.

Breathable waterproof fabrics have very small holes that let sweat vapour out, but the holes are too small to let rainwater droplets in.

How does this dry suit keep the diver warm?

CAN-DO TASK

Level 3 **2** 1

I can make measurements to test a property of a fibre or fabric.

? QUESTIONS

5 Why do fabrics need to be stretchy?

6 How could you test the strength of a thread?

7 Give **one** disadvantage of a waterproof fabric.

8 How do breathable waterproof fabrics work?

CHALLENGE QUESTION

9 How do dry suits keep a diver dry and warm?

key words: breathable   flexible   stretchy   strong   waterproof

Flameproofing

Firefighters depend on their clothing to save their lives. Their clothing needs to be flameproof.

All fibres burn if they get hot enough. Flameproofing works by coating fibres with special chemicals. These chemicals mean the fabric takes longer to catch fire.

The table shows some results when different fabrics are flameproofed. The time in seconds is shown of how long it takes to set each fabric on fire.

What properties do these firefighter's clothes need to have?

Fabric	No treatment (s)	Alum (s)	Borax (s)	Ammonium sulfate (s)
cotton	30	35	39	34
nylon	23	25	28	26
wool	25	32	37	33

Flameproofing in the home

Since 1988 UK law states that all new sofas must be made from flameproof fabrics. Older sofas contain fabrics that could set on fire if a burning cigarette is dropped on them.

When sofas burn, they release lots of choking black smoke that suffocates people. Just as many people die from suffocation in fires as die from burns.

Most homes now have smoke alarms. Smoke alarms have saved many lives. They should be tested every week to make sure they are working. Most smoke alarms 'beep' when the battery needs changing.

What needs to be checked regularly in the smoke alarm to make sure it is working?

? QUESTIONS

10 What needs to be done to flameproof a fabric?

11 In the table above:

   a) Which chemical works best as a flameproofer?

   b) How much longer does it take to set fire to cotton treated with alum compared to untreated cotton?

12 How often should smoke alarms be checked?

CHALLENGE QUESTION

13 How do smoke alarms save lives?

key words: flameproof chemical   smoke alarm   suffocate

First aid

Every school, office and place of work needs to have a first aid kit and someone who is trained to use it.

First aid kits mainly contain plasters, bandages, wound dressings and disposable gloves. This is because the most common minor injuries are cuts or grazes.

Slings are made from cotton because cotton fibres do not stretch very much. Conforming bandages contain cotton and elastic fibres. These mould themselves to the skin to put pressure on wounds. They also stay in place better.

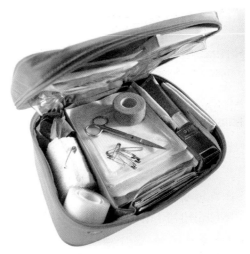

Where would you find a first aid kit?

Treating a wound

Any wound that is bleeding should be cleaned using running water and then dried.

Small cuts can be treated by sticking a plaster on. Bigger wounds need to covered using a bandage or wound dressing. Covering the wound helps to prevent infection.

The bandage or dressing needs to be comfortably tight to put pressure on the wound to help stop the bleeding. Wound dressings have a cotton pad in them to absorb blood.

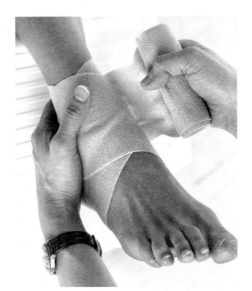

Why should a bandage not be applied too tightly?

Allergies

Different types of fabrics are used in different plasters.

Some people, mainly children, are allergic to the sticky adhesive in some plasters. If an allergic reaction happens, an itchy rash forms on the skin. If you are allergic to one type of plaster, make sure you do not use it.

?QUESTIONS

14 Name **three** items first aid kits contain.

15 Why are arm slings made from cotton?

16 What happens if you are allergic to a plaster?

CHALLENGE QUESTION:

17 Why are disposable gloves needed in a first aid kit?

---

key words: adhesive   allergy   bandage   plaster   wound dressing

REVIEWING THE METHOD

Stretching fibres

Ahmed is going to test the strength of different fibres.

This is his plan.

1 Set the apparatus up as shown in the diagram.
2 Add weights until the thread snaps.
3 Count the weights and write them down.
4 Do it again with a different thread.

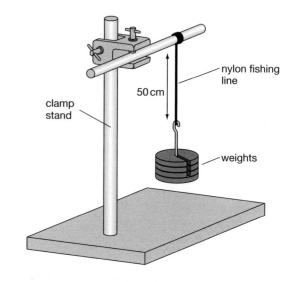

Thread	1st try	2nd try	Mean
cotton	250 g	300 g	275 g
silk	400 g	600 g	
polyester	300 g	400 g	

YOUR TASK

1 Work out the missing mean (average) results.
2 Which result has the largest range?
3 What does a large range say about the method?
4 What could Ahmed have added to his plan to make the method a fairer test?
5 How could Ahmed improve his results?

Maths Skills

Level ③ 2 1

Calculate arithmetical means.

C5 CHECKLIST

I have learnt that...

- ✓ examples of natural fibres are cotton, wool and silk.

- ✓ an example of an artificial fibre is nylon.

- ✓ artificial fibres are also called synthetic fibres as they are man-made using chemical reactions.

- ✓ labels give information about what clothes are made from.

- ✓ the strength and stretch of fibres can be measured.

- ✓ fibres like Gore-Tex® are both waterproof and breathable.

- ✓ breathable fabrics are an advantage for clothing worn for outdoor activities.

- ✓ some chemicals can be used to make fabrics flameproof.

- ✓ flameproofing is measured by how long is takes a fabric to catch fire.

- ✓ some people are allergic to some fabrics.

- ✓ fibres and fabrics used in health care must not harm the body.

I can ...

- ✓ give examples where artificial fibres have replaced natural fibres.

- ✓ interpret information from labels on clothes.

- ✓ give an advantage and a disadvantage of waterproof clothing.

- ✓ make measurements to test a property of a fibre or fabric
  ➥CAN-DO TASK Level ②.

- ✓ interpret data I am given about waterproof and flameproof fabrics.

- ✓ interpret data about the use of fabrics and fibres in health care.

Clean air

I am an Environmental Health Officer

I work for the local council. Part of my job is to monitor air quality from traffic and industry to meet targets set by the government.

In my job, I need to check air quality every day. I do this on my computer using results from air quality monitoring stations in my area. I am working on methods to reduce traffic in areas where pollution is higher. Poor air quality can cause health problems for people.

Earth's atmosphere

The atmosphere is made up of air. The atmosphere is a very thin layer of gases that surrounds our planet.

The atmosphere thins out very quickly above the Earth. You would have difficulty breathing above 8 km, which is less than the height of Mount Everest.

Air contains a mixture of gases. Nitrogen is the main gas but it does very little. Oxygen is the gas we need to breathe to stay alive and it is also needed for burning.

The remaining 1% of air is a mixture of argon, carbon dioxide and other gases. Carbon dioxide is needed for plants to grow. The atmosphere also contains water, which forms droplets or ice crystals in clouds.

The thin blue line shows our atmosphere. What is in the atmosphere?

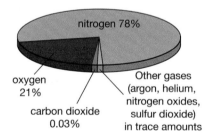

nitrogen 78%

oxygen 21%

carbon dioxide 0.03%

Other gases (argon, helium, nitrogen oxides, sulfur dioxide) in trace amounts

The gases that make up air.

❓ QUESTIONS

1 Which gas is about 0.03% of the air?

2 Which gas do we need to live?

3 Why do climbers use oxygen bottles on Everest?

CHALLENGE QUESTION

4 Why is water not included in the air pie chart?

key words: atmosphere   mixture   nitrogen   oxygen

Burning fuels

All the fuels we burn contain carbon. Fossil fuels are coal, oil and gas. These fuels contain chemicals called hydrocarbons. Fuels need oxygen to burn. When any fuel burns the carbon joins with oxygen from the air to make carbon dioxide gas and water.

Burning can be written as a word equation:

fuel + oxygen → carbon dioxide + water

What substances are made when natural gas burns?

Testing for carbon dioxide

Carbon dioxide gas can be tested by bubbling it though a clear colourless chemical called limewater. If carbon dioxide is present the limewater turns milky (cloudy white).

Global warming

Small amounts of carbon dioxide gas in our atmosphere help to keep the planet warm enough to live on. Without it we would freeze to death.

Colourless clear limewater.

Carbon dioxide turns limewater milky.

But too much carbon dioxide causes global warming by trapping heat in the atmosphere. If our planet warms too much, the climate will change and sea levels will rise as the ice caps melt. Evidence shows the amount of carbon dioxide in the atmosphere is increasing.

CAN-DO TASK

Level 3 ② 1

I can carry out a test to show the presence of carbon dioxide.

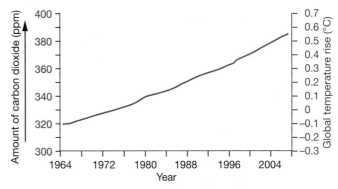

What is happening to the amount of carbon dioxide in the atmosphere?

? QUESTIONS

5 Name **two** substances that are made when a fuel burns.

6 a) Which chemical is used to test for carbon dioxide?

   b) What do you see if carbon dioxide is bubbled though this chemical?

7 How does carbon dioxide cause global warming?

CHALLENGE QUESTION:

8 Carbon dioxide in the atmosphere has good and bad effects. What are they?

key words: carbon   carbon dioxide   fossil fuel   global warming

Air pollution

All fuels contain small amounts of chemicals that add to air pollution when the fuel burns. Air pollution is made when harmful chemicals are released into the air. These harmful chemicals are called pollutants.

Nitrogen oxides

When a fuel burns at a high temperature in a car engine, nitrogen and oxygen from the air join together to make nitrogen oxides. Nitrogen oxides can trigger asthma attacks, breathing problems and cause acid rain.

Carbon particles

If a fuel does not burn completely, carbon particles escape into the air. If these are breathed in, they can cause lung damage. When the black specks of carbon land they can make buildings dirty.

How does industry cause air pollution?

Sulfur dioxide

All fuels contain a small amount of sulfur. When the fuel burns, the sulfur joins with oxygen to make sulfur dioxide. Sulfur dioxide can trigger asthma attacks and cause acid rain.

Acid rain

Nitrogen oxides and sulfur dioxide gases dissolve in water to make acids. This can happen in clouds. When the acid rain falls on the soil or into lakes, it makes the soil or water more acid. This can kill plants and animals.

Winds can carry the acid rain huge distances.

How has acid rain killed these trees?

? QUESTIONS

9 What are pollutants?

10 Name **two** pollutants that can trigger asthma attacks in people.

11 How does acid rain form?

CHALLENGE QUESTION:

12 Why do countries like Germany and Poland blame Britain for killing their forests?

key words: acid rain   nitrogen oxides   pollutant   sulfur dioxide

Reducing car pollution

Car engines produce a lot of pollutants. In some cities, the air quality is so bad people choose to wear masks.

To reduce pollution, some cities have introduced congestion charges to try and reduce the amount of traffic.

What does this mask do?

Catalytic converters

Catalytic converters contain a catalyst. Catalysts speed up reactions without being used up. Catalytic converters remove three pollutant gases:

♦ nitrogen oxides are changed to non-polluting nitrogen gas;

♦ poisonous carbon monoxide is changed into non-poisonous carbon dioxide gas;

♦ unburnt hydrocarbons from the fuel are removed.

Disadvantages of catalytic converters

Catalytic converters also have disadvantages. They add to the cost of a new car and are expensive to replace. They also reduce the miles per litre of the car.

They cannot be used in older cars that need petrol containing lead. Lead and zinc metal, found in some oils destroy the catalyst, making it useless.

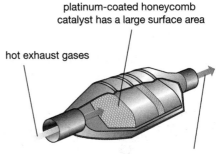

platinum-coated honeycomb catalyst has a large surface area

hot exhaust gases

carbon dioxide, nitrogen and water

A catalytic converter.

MOT tests

Cars over three years old need to have a yearly MOT test.

Exhaust emissions levels are part of this test. If the catalytic converter is not working, the car will fail the test.

? QUESTIONS

13 What is a catalyst?

14 Name **three** pollutants removed by a catalytic converter.

15 How often do cars over three years old need an MOT test?

CHALLENGE QUESTION:

16 Carbon monoxide has the chemical formula, CO. What must happen to it to change it into carbon dioxide, CO_2?

---

key words: catalyst   catalytic converter   MOT test   platinum

PROCESSING THE DATA

How far does soot travel from car exhausts?

Soot particles are small pieces of carbon. They are given out by car exhausts.

Fiona and Jay think these pieces do not travel very far.

To test this, they put soot collectors differerent distances from a road. The nearest was at 2 metres, the furthest at 10 metres.

After a day they collected the soot collectors.

The diagram shows their results.

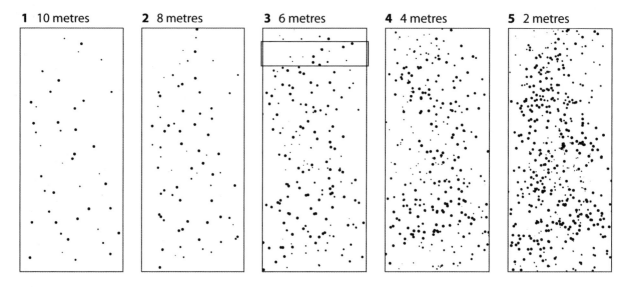

| **1** 10 metres | **2** 8 metres | **3** 6 metres | **4** 4 metres | **5** 2 metres |

Fiona and Jay know that there are too many spots to count them all. They decide to just count some spots using a see-through plastic strip, as shown in slide 3.

Maths Skills

Level 3 **②** 1

Estimate quantities such as length, volume or mass.

Maths Skills

Level 3 2 **①**

Draw bar charts.

🖊 YOUR TASK

1 Fiona and Jay counted 38 spots on slide 5 and 24 spots on slide 4. How many do you think they counted on the other slides?

2 Show your estimates in a table.

3 Draw a bar chart of your estimates.

C6 CHECKLIST

I have learnt that...

✓ the atmosphere is a mixture of gases.

✓ air contains about 80% nitrogen and 20% oxygen.

✓ the atmosphere surrounds Earth and contains air, water and small amounts of harmful pollutants.

✓ fuels contain carbon, which is released as carbon dioxide when fuels burn.

✓ the amount of carbon dioxide in the air is increasing and this is linked to global warming.

✓ fuels contain small amounts of sulfur that is released as sulfur dioxide when the fuels burn.

✓ nitrogen and oxygen from the air join to make nitrogen oxides in hot car engines.

✓ nitrogen oxides and sulfur dioxide are linked to asthma and acid rain.

✓ carbon particles (soot) from car exhausts are linked to lung disease.

✓ catalytic converters remove some pollutants from exhaust gases.

✓ exhaust gases are checked during an MOT test.

I can ...

✓ interpret information given to me about air quality.

✓ carry out a test to show the presence of carbon dioxide
⟫ CAN-DO TASK Level ②.

✓ plan to measure how carbon particles decrease with distance from a road.

✓ state the benefits and drawbacks of using a catalytic converter.

Strong stuff

I am a sports equipment designer

I design different rackets for squash, tennis, badminton and table tennis. I need to design equipment that looks good and works well. Cost is a big factor in my work. Professional players are happy to spend lots of money on equipment that works for them. Amateurs want something that works without costing too much.

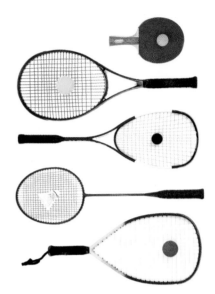

I need to understand the physical properties of materials like strength, hardness and flexibility. I also need to know which materials I can put together to make alloys and composites.

Physical properties

Metals and non-metals have different properties. Property is the scientific word for how a material behaves.

The table shows what most metal and non-metals do, but there are a few exceptions. Graphite is a non-metal that conducts electricity. Lead is a soft metal. Plastics are non-metals, but some are flexible, or ductile, when heated.

Why are these wires covered with coloured plastic insulators?

Metals	Non-metals
conductors (heat and electricity)	insulators (heat and electricity)
hard (cannot be scratched)	soft
strong (do not break easily)	weak
flexible (bend without snapping)	brittle (snap)
ductile (can be pulled and shaped)	rigid
shiny	dull

? QUESTIONS

1 Which property means metals cannot be scratched?
2 What is the opposite of brittle?
3 Give **two** reasons electrical wires are covered in plastic.

CHALLENGE QUESTION:

4 Suggest why graphite is classed as a non-metal.

key words: conduct   ductile   flexible   hard   insulate   property

Alloys

An alloy is a mixture of a metal element with another element.

Some examples of alloys are:

♦ steel for making bridges, ships and lorries
♦ solder for joining electrical components
♦ aluminium alloy for aircraft and bike frames
♦ brass for musical instruments and money.

Alloys have different properties from the elements they are made from. Copper is brown and zinc is silvery. Mixing these makes brass, which has a golden colour.

A brass trumpet – which two elements make brass?

Smart alloys

Nitinol metal is smart alloy made by mixing nickel and titanium. It is a memory shape alloy. Frames for glasses can be made from nitinol. If the frame gets bent out of shape, putting it into hot water changes it back to its original shape.

Smart alloy wires are being used in robots. An electric current can be used to heat the wires making them move. When the wires cool they return to their original shape.

Bent smart alloy frames can be returned to their original shape by putting them in hot water.

Measuring hardness

If an iron nail is rubbed on limestone rock, the limestone is scratched and bits flake off. This method can be used to compare how hard different materials are. If two rocks are rubbed together, the weaker one is scratched and flakes off.

Some rocks like diamond, rubies and sapphires are very hard. This is why they are used in jewellery. Diamond is the hardest substance known, so it will scratch everything else.

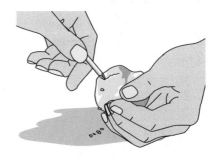

Testing the hardness of limestone rock.

? QUESTIONS

5 How can you change the properties of a metal?

6 Which alloy is used to make a trumpet?

7 What do smart alloys do?

8 Describe how to test for hardness.

CHALLENGE QUESTION:

9 Describe how you could test if an alloy is a smart alloy.

key words: alloy   hardness   mixture   smart alloy

Rocks as raw materials

Granite, limestone and marble are raw materials used for building. They are rocks that are mined or quarried from the Earth. They are used because they are strong, hard and attractive.

- ♦ Granite is used on the outside of buildings and for kitchen worktops.
- ♦ Limestone is used for buildings like churches.
- ♦ Marble is used for the outside of buildings, and for statues and columns.

Brick

Most houses in Britain are made from stone or brick. Bricks are easier to build with, as they are all the same shape. Bricks are made from clay. Clay is a mineral dug out of the ground. To make bricks the clay needs to be dried, shaped and baked in an oven.

Cement, mortar and concrete

Cement is a powder made of a mixture of limestone and clay. It is a binder which means it is like glue. Cement is used to make mortar and concrete.

Bricks need to be joined together using mortar. Mortar is made by mixing cement with sand and adding water. The exact mix depends on the job. The more cement that is used, the stronger the mix, but the more it costs.

Concrete is made by mixing cement, sand, small stones and water. Concrete is used to cover large areas like paths and drives. Concrete can be made stronger by pouring it around a steel cage or steel bars. This is called reinforced concrete.

A marble quarry in Italy. What might this marble be used for?

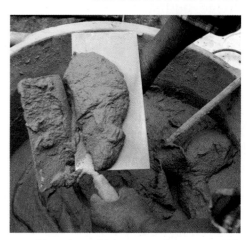

How has this mortar been made?

? QUESTIONS

10 Name **two** ways to extract rocks from the Earth.

11 Why are bricks easier to build with than stone?

12 What is reinforced concrete?

CHALLENGE QUESTION:

13 Write a plan to test the strength of different mortars.

key words: brick   cement   concrete   granite   limestone   marble

What is the best material?

The table shows information about materials used to make tennis rackets. Density is mass divided by volume.

The lower the density, the less the racket will weigh.

Wooden rackets are made using different types of wood to give good flexibility, but they are not very strong. Metal rackets are strong. Steel can rust and is heavy.

Aluminium alloy is not as strong as steel, but it is less dense. Carbon fibre (graphite) rackets are very strong with a low density, but they cost much more than the other materials.

Material	Density in g/cm³	Strength (1 = weakest)
wood	0.7	3
aluminium alloy	2.8	6
steel	7.8	8
carbon fibre	2.3	15

What properties does a racket frame need?

Composite materials

Plywood is made by gluing thin sheets of wood together. The sheets are placed so the grain is at right angles to the layer above and below. This increases the strength.

Plywood contains wood and glue. When two or more materials are used together, a new composite material is made. Plywood is used for loft boarding. It can also be made waterproof for outdoor use like in wooden boat panels.

How are the layers of this plywood arranged and what holds them together?

Another composite material is glass reinforced plastic (GRP) or fibreglass. GRP is used to make cycle shelters and boat decks. Reinforced concrete is another composite material.

? QUESTIONS

14 What needs to be measured to work out density?

15 Give **one** advantage and **one** disadvantage of using steel for a tennis racket.

16 Give a use for **a)** GRP **b)** plywood **c)** reinforced concrete.

CHALLENGE QUESTION:

17 Why are composite materials better than a single material?

key words: composite   density   flexibility   mass   volume

PLANNING TO COLLECT DATA

Making and testing mortar

Mortar is used to join bricks together.

You need to plan an experiment to find out how changing the mortar mixture affects its strength.

Basic mortar contains 3 parts sand to 1 part cement.

You can measure out the sand and cement using a spoon.

The sand and cement are mixed together, and then water is added to make the mortar.

Too much water makes it sloppy, but too little means it will not set well.

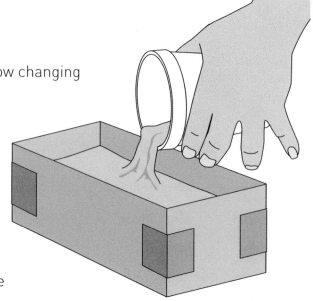

YOUR TASK

1 Why do all the blocks need to be the same size?

2 How will you make sure the blocks are the same size?

3 You will need to make four different mixes. Complete a table like the one below to show your different mixes.

Mix	Spoons of sand	Spoons of cement	Total spoons
A	3	1	4
B			
C			
D			

4 How will you make sure the sand and cement are fully mixed?

5 How will you decide how much water to use?

6 How will you know when your mortar has set?

7 How will you test the strength of your mortar mixes?

CAN-DO TASK

Level **3** 2 1

I can make and then test a sample of mortar for its strength.

Maths Skills

Level 3 2 **1**

Carry out simple calculations.

C7 CHECKLIST

I have learnt that...

✓ metals conduct heat and electricity, are hard, strong, flexible and shiny.

✓ non-metals are insulators of heat and electricity, soft, weak, brittle, rigid and dull.

✓ alloys contain a metal mixed with another element and have different properties to the elements they are made from.

✓ smart alloys change shape with temperature.

✓ some hard minerals are used to make jewellery.

✓ granite, limestone and marble are extracted from the Earth, and used as building materials because they are hard and strong.

✓ bricks are made by heating clay.

✓ concrete is made from sand, cement, small stones and water.

✓ wood, metal and carbon fibres can be used to make sports equipment.

✓ composites contain two different materials.

I can ...

✓ decide if a substance is a metal or non-metal by testing its physical properties.

✓ name and give uses of four different alloys.

✓ interpret information given to me linking the properties of materials to their uses.

✓ use a key to rank materials in order of hardness.

✓ give one advantage and one disadvantage of using wood, metals and carbon fibre for sports equipment.

✓ compare the strength of different concrete or mortar samples.

✓ make and test a sample of mortar for its strength.
➦ **CAN-DO TASK** Level ③

✓ name and give a use for three composite materials.

Restless Earth

I am a geologist

I study rocks. Rocks tell us how the land formed and how it has changed over time. Rocks are always being made and destroyed. Volcanoes make new rock. Earthquakes and some volcanic eruptions are happening all the time, but only a few are large enough to make the news.

In my job, I am part of a team that collects evidence about when earthquakes or volcanoes might happen. We cannot predict this very accurately, but we know where they might happen in the next 1000 years or so.

The Earth's structure

We live on a sphere called the Earth. The land we live on and the sea floor make up the Earth's crust. It only extends down a few kilometres. Below this is a sea of liquid rock called the mantle. The average temperature in the mantle is around 5400 °C. At the centre of the Earth is the core. It contains nickel and iron and gives the Earth its magnetic field.

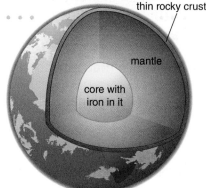

thin rocky crust

mantle

core with iron in it

The Earth's structure.

Tectonic plates

The crust and top semi-solid part of the mantle are split into sections called tectonic plates. These plates move very slowly. Some plates are moving apart, some rub along each other and some are moving towards each other (colliding). Most earthquakes and volcanoes happen where plates meet.

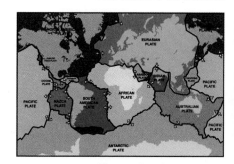

Tectonic plates map.

? QUESTIONS

1 What is the mantle?

2 Which part of the Earth floats on the mantle?

3 What do collisions between plates cause?

CHALLENGE QUESTION:

4 Britain is moving away from America at about 1 cm per year. How far will they have moved apart by 2500?

key words: core   crust   mantle   sphere   tectonic plate

Earthquakes

During an earthquake, a large amount of energy is suddenly released. This happens when tectonic plates collide or rub together. Pressure builds up until huge sections of rock snap.

An earthquake releases shockwaves that shake the Earth's surface. Buildings and services like water and gas supplies can all be damaged. Landslides can destroy roads. This often makes it difficult to send help and supplies to affected areas.

Major earthquakes are often followed by aftershocks. These cause further damage to already weakened buildings. Aftershocks are smaller earthquakes caused by plates settling.

Effects on people and animals

In major earthquakes people die by being buried or hit by falling buildings. After an earthquake, rescue teams try to find people and dig them out. In remote areas, water, food and shelter are often hard to find.

Earthquakes destroy habitats. Forests can be knocked down, lakes can drain away and crops can be destroyed. This affects wildlife as well as humans.

Earthquake warnings

If an earthquake happens under the sea, a large wave called a tsunami can form. When a tsunami reaches land, the wave can flood the land.

It is not possible to predict exactly when an earthquake might happen. Areas at risk often have plans in place to tell people what to do when an earthquake hits. Authourities in earthquake risk areas recommend keeping an emergency kit including a battery powered radio and torch with spare batteries. If you are inside, you are advised to shelter under tables or doorframes. If you are outside you should try to find open space away from buildings that could collapse.

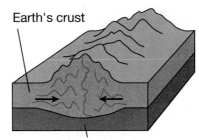

Earthquake's can happen when plates move towards each other.

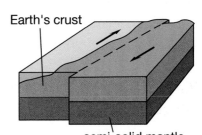

Earthquake's can happen when plates rub together.

CAN-DO TASK

Level **3** 2 1

I can find the location of 10 earthquakes or volcanoes and put them on a map.

? QUESTIONS

5 What is released when an earthquake takes place?

6 What are aftershocks?

7 What is a tsunami?

CHALLENGE QUESTION

8 Find the names of plates that are moving apart, colliding, and rubbing against each other.

key words: aftershock   earthquake   landslide   tsunami

Volcanoes

Volcanoes form when molten magma finds it way to the surface from the mantle. This can happen when tectonic plates move apart (diagram A), or when one plate sinks below another (diagram B).

Molten magma erupting from a volcano is called lava. Volcanoes also release ash and gases. Some volcanoes explode violently and some erupt gently depending on what the magma contains.

Volcanoes form into cones as the lava and ash builds up over many eruptions.

Living near volcanoes

Major volcanic eruptions don't happen very often, but if they do there are risks. People can be killed if a volcano explodes. They are poisoned by the gases or choked by ash, and have their homes destroyed by lava.

But there are also benefits:
♦ buying land is usually fairly cheap
♦ heat from new rocks can be used to heat homes
♦ the ash is a good fertiliser to grow crops.

Igneous rocks

Igneous rocks contain different minerals.

The type of igneous rock formed from lava depends on the cooling rate. The faster it cools, the smaller the crystals are.

When granite forms, the minerals cool slowly, forming large crystals that lock together. This gives granite its speckled effect. In basalt, fast cooling makes crystals that are too small to see.

Liquid rock flowing along the surface is called lava. It cools quickly and forms rock called basalt that has small crystals.

Liquid rock that never reaches the surface is called magma. It cools slowly and forms rock called granite that has large crystals.

Cross-section of a volcano.

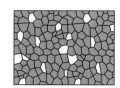

Fast cooling makes small crystals.

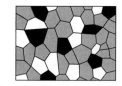

Slow cooling makes large crystals.

? QUESTIONS

9 What is the difference between magma and lava?

10 Name **three** substances released during a volcanic eruption.

11 Describe how a volcanic cone builds up.

CHALLENGE QUESTION:

12 How do plate movements cause volcanoes?

---

key words: crystal   igneous   lava   magma   volcano

Continental drift

Rocks show that Scotland was not always joined to England. Rocks also show that South America might have once been joined to Africa.

The idea that whole continents can move was first suggested by Alfred Wegener in 1915. He called this idea continental drift.

Wegener used the following evidence for his idea:

♦ continents can be fitted together like a jigsaw so at one time they must have all been joined up

♦ fossils found in South America and Africa match

♦ rocks in South America and Africa match.

200 million years ago

Today

How Wegener suggested the continents have moved (continental drift).

The science debate

Many scientists at the time did not accept Wegener's ideas. He could not prove continents were moving, as it took place too slowly to measure. Matching rocks could be explained if a land bridge once extended from Africa to South America.

Animals could have crossed the bridge, and this could explain the similar fossils.

New evidence

Today satellite measurements show continents are moving. New evidence has also come from exploration of the sea floor.

Magnetic measurements have shown the sea floor in the mid-Atlantic is spreading apart. It is now believed that 250 million years ago almost all the land fitted together in one super continent called Pangaea.

Over millions of years the continents have drifted to where they are today. Most scientists now accept Wegener's ideas.

Pangaea. How many years ago would Earth have looked like this?

? QUESTIONS

13 What is continental drift?

14 What evidence did Wegener use for his idea?

15 What new evidence supports the idea of continental drift?

CHALLENGE QUESTION:

16 What is needed for a scientific theory (idea) to be accepted?

key words: Alfred Wegener   continental drift   evidence   exploration

PROCESSING DATA

Melting wax

Magma needs to to be a liquid to erupt from a volcano. This can be modelled using wax.

Josh and Sanjay planned to see how changing the temperature changed the time for 5 g of paraffin wax to melt completely. They knew that paraffin wax melts at 44 °C.

Here are Josh and Sanjay's results:

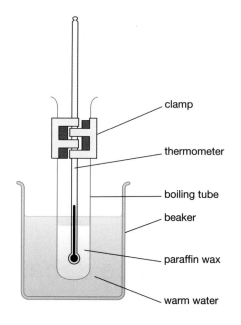

Temperature in °C	Time in seconds
45	400
50	330
55	350
60	150
65	50

YOUR TASK

1 One of the results is not correct.
   Which one do you think it is?
2 Draw a bar chart to show the results.
   ● What will go on the bottom axis?
   ● What will go on the side axis?
   ● What scale will you use?
   ● What title will you put on your chart?
3 Now draw a line graph to show the results.
4 How could you make sure your graph is correct?
5 What pattern does the data show?

CAN-DO TASK
Level 3 2 ①

I can add results to a bar chart.

Maths Skills
Level 3 2 ①

Draw or complete bar charts or pictograms.

C8 CHECKLIST

I have learnt that...

- ✓ the Earth is a sphere with core, mantle and crust.
- ✓ the rocky crust and top part of the mantle are split into tectonic plates.
- ✓ earthquakes and volcanoes are linked to plate movements.
- ✓ earthquakes release energy as shock waves.
- ✓ underwater earthquakes may cause tsunamis.
- ✓ earthquakes effect both people and wildlife.
- ✓ it is impossible to exactly predict earthquakes.
- ✓ molten rock in the mantle is magma, but when it escapes from a volcano it becomes lava.
- ✓ igneous rock that cools quickly from lava forms basalt, which has very small crystals.
- ✓ igneous rock that cools slowly underground makes granite, which has larger crystals.
- ✓ there are risks and benefits of living near a volcano.

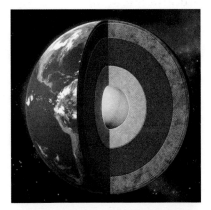

I can ...

- ✓ plot the position of 10 earthquakes or volcanoes onto a map
  ⟶CAN-DO TASK Level ③.
- ✓ give advice about keeping safe in an earthquake.
- ✓ describe evidence to support the idea of continental drift.
- ✓ link the cooling time of igneous rocks to crystal size.
- ✓ give advantages and disadvantages of living near a volcano.

How fast? How slow?

I am a firework display designer

I work with bands and festival organisers. Many bands and festival organisers want fireworks to be used as part of their event. Sometimes these need to be matched to music.

For my job I need to know about the reaction rates of the fireworks I use. Getting this right is the main part of a display. Once I get it all planned, I use computers to make sure the timing is right.

Reaction rates

Chemical reactions happen at different rates. Some, like explosions, are very fast and are measured in fractions of a second. Rusting takes days and chemical weathering by acid rain takes many years. Science experiments need to happen at a rate that can be measured easily.

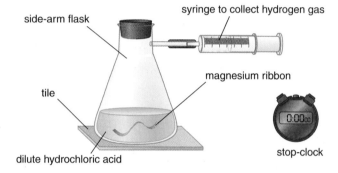

side-arm flask

syringe to collect hydrogen gas

magnesium ribbon

tile

dilute hydrochloric acid

stop-clock

Monitoring reactions

Some chemical reactions take in or give out a gas. For example, when magnesium and dilute hydrochloric acid react, they give off hydrogen gas. We can monitor reactions like this by:

♦ using a balance to measure changes in mass

♦ using a measuring cylinder or syringe to measure changes in volume.

Most chemical reactions start off quickly and then slow down as the reactants are used up, as shown in the graph.

Hydrogen gas can be collected and measured with this apparatus.

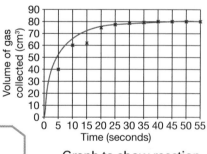

Graph to show reaction of magnesium with hydrochloric acid.

CAN-DO TASK

Level 3 2 **1**

I can measure reaction time.

? QUESTIONS

1 Name **two** very fast chemical reactions.

2 Name **two** ways to monitor reactions.

3 Why do reactions slow down?

CHALLENGE QUESTION:

4 Describe the pattern shown by the graph above.

---

key words: mass   monitor   reactant   reaction rate   volume

Changing temperature

Temperature measures how hot a substance is and is measured in °C. Increasing the temperature speeds up most chemical reactions. Particles move faster and collide more often. Lowering the temperature slows down most chemical reactions. Putting food in a fridge or freezer slows down the changes that make it go bad.

The experiment shown in the diagram can be used to investigate reaction rates.

To change the temperature safely, the flask and acid need to be put into a beaker of hot water. When the temperature you want has been reached, add the magnesium, fit the bung and collect the gas.

This apparatus can be used to find how changing temperature changes the rate a gas is made.

Changing concentration

Concentration is about how much of a substance is dissolved in the same amount of water. A high concentration has lots of substance dissolved, and a low concentration has little substance dissolved. Increasing the concentration increases the reaction rate as there are more particles to collide.

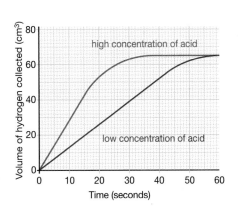

Graph to show how concentration affects reaction rate.

CAN-DO TASK

Level 3 2 **1**

I can use a measuring cylinder to measure volume.

CAN-DO TASK

Level **3** 2 1

I can measure time accurately (e.g. to time a chemical reaction).

? QUESTIONS

5 a) What does increasing temperature do to the reaction rate?

   b) Why does this happen?

6 a) What does increasing concentration do to the reaction rate?

   b) Why does this happen?

CHALLENGE QUESTION:

7 A solution has 50 g dissolved in 100 cm³ of water. How could you make a solution with half the concentration?

---

key words: collide   concentration   particle   temperature

Surface area

Chemical reactions take place when particles collide. This means that in solids, reactions can only take place on the surfaces.

If an acid is added to a solid like magnesium, the moving particles in the liquid acid collide with the surface of the lump of magnesium. All the magnesium on the inside is protected until the surface layer is removed by the reaction.

If the magnesium is cut up into smaller pieces, more surfaces are made. This means more collisions can take place in the same time. Breaking up solids makes the reaction rate faster.

The more a solid is cut up, the larger the surface area becomes.

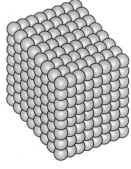

In a solid lump most of the particles are inside.

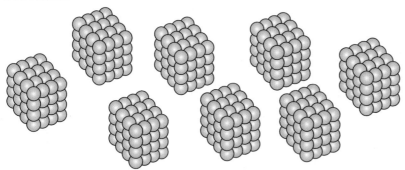

Cutting the solid means it has more surfaces.

Using surface area

Here are some examples of why changing the surface area is useful or dangerous.

♦ cutting up carrots into bits makes them cook faster
♦ flour dust in the air in flour mills can explode
♦ coal dust in mines can explode
♦ small lumps of charcoal burn faster than large lumps
♦ sugar grains dissolve faster than sugar lumps.

Which dust could have caused this explosion at a factory?

? QUESTIONS

8 Why do reactions only happen at surfaces?

9 What happens to the surface area when a solid is cut up?

10 Why is dust a problem in factories?

CHALLENGE QUESTION:

11 Why is fine dust more likely to explode than a solid?

key words: collide   particle   reaction   surface area

Catalysts

Catalysts are:

♦ substances that speed up a reaction

♦ not used up in the reaction

♦ only needed in small amounts.

Each catalyst speeds up just one reaction. An example is a chemical called manganese oxide. It acts as a catalyst to break down hydrogen peroxide into oxygen and water. Without the catalyst the reaction is very slow.

Another example is a chemical called copper sulfate. It acts as a catalyst to speed up the reaction between zinc and sulfuric acid to make zinc sulfate and hydrogen. Without adding the copper sulfate, the reaction is quite slow.

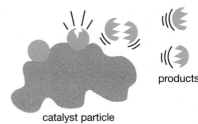

How a catalyst works.

How catalysts work

Catalysts work by providing a site where the reactants can meet to react. The products then move away, leaving the site free for the next reactants to move in.

Epoxy resin

Snowboards, surf boards and skate boards are all made out of epoxy resin. To make the resin you need the resin and a catalyst called the hardener. The resin will go hard on its own, but it takes a very long time. The catalyst speeds up the setting time.

Some strong glues use this idea. To make the glue set quickly, the resin and hardener are mixed together. The bar chart shows the time for resin to set with different amounts of hardener.

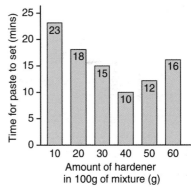

Time taken for resin to set with different amounts of hardener.

? QUESTIONS

12 State **three** things about catalysts.

13 a) Which catalyst speeds up the reaction between zinc and sulfuric acid?

b) Why would manganese oxide not speed up this reaction?

14 Use the graph above to find out how long the resin takes to set with 30 g of hardener in the mixture.

CHALLENGE QUESTION:

15 Describe how a catalyst works.

---

key words: catalyst   epoxy resin   product   reactant

INTERPRETING DATA

Temperature and reaction time

Jess and Deon timed the reaction between magnesium and dilute hydrochloric acid. They used the same amount of magnesium and acid, but changed the temperature.

Here are their results:

Temperature in °C	Time for the magnesium to disappear in seconds			
	1st try	2nd try	3rd try	Mean
20	135	120	105	120
30	89	96	76	87
40	64	60	62	62
50	46	48	41	45

Jess and Deon made this graph to show their results.

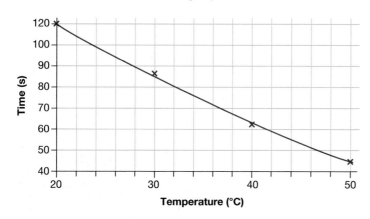

YOUR TASK

1 What was the mean value at 20°C?

2 What range of results did they get at 30°C?

3 What happens to the mean as the temperature goes up?

4 State the trend shown by their results.

5 Use a science idea to explain their results.

6 What do you think about the quality of Jess and Deon's results?

Maths Skills

Level **3** **②** **1**

Read data from graphs.

Maths Skills

Level **3** **②** **1**

Extract and use information from tables and graphs.

C9 CHECKLIST

I have learnt that...

✓ chemical reaction rates can vary greatly.

✓ a reaction stops when a reactant is used up.

✓ reactions start quickly, but then slow down.

✓ increasing temperature usually speeds up a chemical reaction.

✓ lowering temperature slows the changes that make food go bad.

✓ increasing concentration increases the speed of a reaction.

✓ cutting solids into smaller bits speeds up a reaction by increasing the surface area.

✓ catalysts speed up reactions, but are not used up.

✓ particle collisions can be used to explain changes in reaction rates.

I can ...

✓ measure reaction time
➡CAN-DO TASK Level ①.

✓ use a measuring cylinder to measure volume
➡CAN-DO TASK Level ①.

✓ measure time accurately (e.g. to time a chemical reaction)
➡CAN-DO TASK Level ③.

✓ monitor reactions by changes in mass or volume.

✓ interpret information from charts and graphs.

✓ label simple laboratory apparatus.

✓ interpret information about the use of different catalysts.

Sorting out

I am a water engineer

I worked at a water treatment plant making sure water was fit to drink. Water often has chemicals in it, washed in from farms and industry, and these must be removed. Now I work for a charity in Africa. We provide low-cost ways to get safe drinking water to people.

In my job, I need to know about how to find and transport clean water. I need to know about how to separate mixtures, and how to test if the water is pure.

Separating mixtures

A mixture contains two or more substances that are not joined together. As they are not joined, they are fairly easy to separate. To separate a mixture you need to know the properties of the substances in it.

Dissolve, filter, evaporate

This method is used if one substance is soluble (dissolves) and one is insoluble (does not dissolve). To separate the substances, put the mixture in a beaker, add water and stir. This dissolves the soluble substance.

Next filter by pouring it though filter paper. The insoluble substance stays on the filter paper. The soluble substance can be changed back into a solid by evaporating the water. Heating it speeds this up, but it will evaporate in a few days if it is left in a warm room.

Filtering — mixture of soluble and insoluble substances

filter paper

filter funnel

soluble substance

filtrate (liquid)

Evaporating

evaporating basin — crystals begin to form

Apparatus to separate a mixture of soluble and insoluble substances.

CAN-DO TASK

Level 3 2 **1**

I can separate a simple mixture (e.g. sand from salt).

? QUESTIONS

1 Why is it easy to separate mixtures?

2 What do you need to know before you can separate a mixture?

3 How do you separate a soluble and insoluble substance?

CHALLENGE QUESTION:

4 Copper sulfate is soluble. Magnesium oxide is insoluble.

Write a plan to separate a mixture of these substances, so that both end up as solids.

key words: dissolve   evaporate   filter   insoluble   mixture   soluble

Chromatography

Chromatography is used to find out how many different dyes are in a coloured mixture. Chromatography depends on how well each dye dissolves.

The liquid solvent soaks up the paper. It dissolves the soluble dyes and then carries them up the paper. Dyes that are more soluble move up the paper faster. The same dye should move by the same amount in the same time if the same solvent is used.

Chromatography can be used to match paint or ink samples, or to check to see if a food contains allowed chemicals. These chemicals are called E numbers.

The chromatogram shows how far the coloured dye in each E number moves up the paper, and which E numbers are in the food.

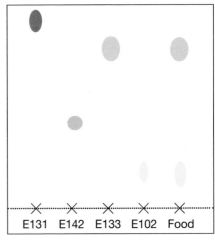

E131   E142   E133   E102   Food

The chromatogram shows different E numbers, and a food.

List some everyday uses of magnets.

CAN-DO TASK

Level   3   **2**   1

I can make a chromatogram.

Magnetism

The only magnetic elements are iron, nickel and cobalt. Steel is also magnetic as it is almost pure iron.

Magnets have many uses. Some are:
♦ magnetic strips on credit cards
♦ compasses for navigating
♦ in electric motors used in machines like drills, hair dryers and food processors
♦ keeping fridges and cupboard doors closed
♦ in toys and decorations like fridge magnets.

? QUESTIONS

5 On the chromatogram above:
a) Which E number does the yellow dot represent?
b) What is the E number for the most soluble food colour?

6 Name **three** magnetic metals.

7 Describe how to separate a mixture of iron and aluminium.

CHALLENGE QUESTION:

8 Explain why dyes separate during chromatography.

key words: chromatogram   chromatography   dye   magnetic   soluble   solvent

Decanting

Decanting is a way to separate a liquid from a solid that has settled at the bottom. Decanting does the same job as filtering, but it does not need any special equipment.
You just pour off the liquid very slowly, leaving the solid (sediment) behind.

Soil pH can be tested by shaking a soil sample with water to dissolve the minerals. After it has settled, the liquid can be poured off, leaving the soil behind.

Decanting water from a mix of water and soil.

Centrifuging

This is another way to separate a solid floating in a liquid. A centrifuge works by spinning tubes around very fast. It compacts the solid materials into the bottom of the tube.

Centrifuging is used in medicine to separate:
 ♦ blood cells from the liquid part of blood, called plasma
 ♦ one type of cell from another
 ♦ viruses, so they can be identified.

How does a centrifuge machine separate solid material from liquid?

Dialysis

The kidneys filter your blood. If the kidneys do not work very well, salts can build up in the body. Dialysis removes salts from blood.

Dialysis uses a machine to filter blood outside the body. Each dialysis session takes about 4 hours. It needs to be done three times a week. About 20 000 people in the UK need dialysis to keep them alive.

Why do some people need dialysis?

? QUESTIONS

9 Why do you pour slowly when decanting?

10 Give **one** medical use of centrifuging.

11 What does dialysis remove?

CHALLENGE QUESTION:

12 Describe the difference between decanting and centrifuging.

key words: centrifuge   decant   dialysis   sediment

Pure water

Tap water is safe to drink, but it is not pure. Tap water and bottled water contain dissolved minerals that add to the taste.

Pure water has only water in it. Only pure water freezes and melts at 0 °C and boils at 100 °C.

Only pure substances have fixed melting and boiling points.

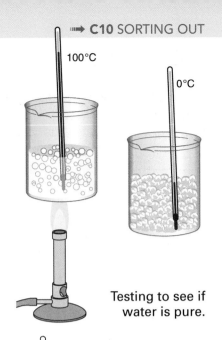

Testing to see if water is pure.

Distillation

In some hot countries there is very little fresh water available. Drinking water can be made from sea-water by using distillation.

Pure water evaporates into steam. The steam is then cooled so it condenses.

Distillation can also be used to separate liquids that have different boiling points, like alcohol and water. Alcohol boils at 78 °C, so has a lower boiling point than water. This means it evaporates first. Distillation is used to make alcoholic drinks like whisky.

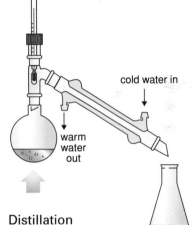

cold water in

warm water out

Distillation equipment.

Melting and boiling points of some substances

Substance	Melting point in °C	Boiling point in °C
carbon	3550	4827
oxygen	−218	−183
aluminium	661	2467
sulfur	113	445
iron	1535	2750
bromine	−7	59

What is happening inside these containers at a whisky distillery?

QUESTIONS

13 What is a test for pure water?

14 Which substance in the table above has the highest boiling point?

15 What happens during distillation?

CHALLENGE QUESTION:

16 Describe how you would separate alcohol and water.

key words: condense   distillation   evaporate   pure water

PATTERNS IN DATA

Does salt change the boiling point of water?

Mike and Suzy want to answer this question.

They boil water in a test tube. It boils at 100 °C.

They put 10 g of salt onto a balance and add it 1 g at a time to the water in the test tube.

They reboil the water and measure the temperature.

The table shows Mike and Suzy's results.

Amount of salt added in g	Boiling temperature in °C
0	100
1	101
2	98
3	103
4	102
5	102
6	101
7	102
8	102
9	103
10	103

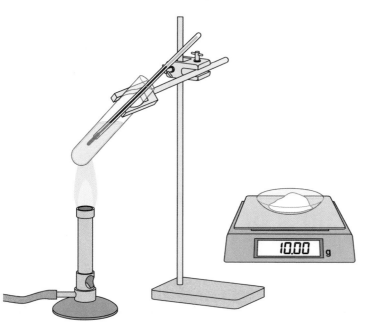

YOUR TASK

Use the results to answer these questions.

1 What was the highest temperature they measured?
2 Which results look like they might not be correct?
3 Suggest a reason why these results might not be correct.
4 By how much did the temperature increase?
5 What pattern is shown by the data?
6 Do you think the results show a clear pattern?

Maths Skills

Level 3 2 **1**

Select information from tables.

Maths Skills

Level 3 **2** 1

Extract and interpret information from tables.

C10 CHECKLIST

I have learnt that...

- ✓ mixtures contain at least two substances that are not joined together and are easy to separate.

- ✓ filtering separates a solid from a solution.

- ✓ chromatography separates coloured dyes.

- ✓ magnets can separate magnetic metals like iron or steel from a mixture.

- ✓ magnets are used in electric motors, compasses, credit card strips and fridge doors.

- ✓ decanting separates a liquid from a solid that has settled.

- ✓ centrifuging separates a solid in a solution by spinning it very fast so the solid settles at the bottom.

- ✓ centrifuging is used to separate blood.

- ✓ dialysis removes salt from the blood.

- ✓ pure water freezes and melts at 0°C and boils at 100°C.

- ✓ distillation is used to get fresh water from salty water and produce alcoholic drinks like whisky.

- ✓ distillation can separate alcohol and water because they have different boiling points.

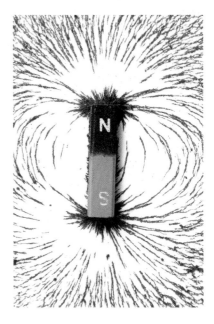

I can ...

- ✓ separate a simple mixture (eg. sand from salt)
  ➠ CAN-DO TASK Level ①.

- ✓ plan how to separate a soluble substance from an insoluble substance.

- ✓ interpret simple chromatograms.

- ✓ make a chromatogram
  ➠ CAN-DO TASK Level ②.

- ✓ interpret information about dialysis.

- ✓ interpret information about melting and boiling points.

CSI plus

I am a scene of crime officer

I work in crime scene investigation (CSI). As a scene of crime officer (SOCO) I work for the police, but I am not a police officer. I work shifts, and I never know where I will be called out next. It could be a serious road traffic accident, a burglary or very occasionally a murder.

My job is about collecting and documenting evidence. I photograph crime scenes and carefully look for evidence. If I find anything, I bag and label the samples. Then I send them off to be analysed. Finally I need to write up my report.

Evidence

Anyone at a crime scene will leave some evidence, even if they are very careful. A hair, a fibre of clothing, dandruff, or a sample of soil might be enough to prove someone was there. Shoe prints or tyre imprints can be left on soft surfaces.

Crime scene investigators need to look very carefully for any evidence. It might take a whole day just to search the inside of a car, but this is better than missing anything. SOCOs need to be very patient and thorough.

Why do evidence bags need lots of details written onto them?

Protecting the evidence

SOCOs need to be careful not to damage or contaminate the evidence, so they wear special clothing like shoe covers, plastic overalls with hoods and gloves.

If any evidence is found it needs to be placed in an evidence bag and carefully labelled. The label will say what it is, where it was collected, who collected it, and give the date and time.

? QUESTIONS

1 What does 'SOCO' stand for?

2 Name **four** ways evidence can be left at a crime scene.

3 Why does evidence need to be bagged and labelled?

CHALLENGE QUESTION:

4 Describe why contaminated evidence is bad.

key words: contaminate   crime scene   evidence   investigator

Fingerprints

If you touch a surface, the oils on your skin leave a mark. Dusting with a special fine powder can show up this mark as a fingerprint. If you press hard, you will leave a full print.

If you move your finger about, the fingerprint might get smeared making it more difficult to see. Wearing gloves stops fingerprints being left. Fingerprints can be removed from hard surfaces by rubbing them with a cloth, but they are easy to miss as they cannot be seen.

What makes this fingerprint show up?

Showing up fingerprints

Different methods can be used to show up fingerprints at a crime scene. The method used depends on the surface.

Dusting with powder or using sticky tape is best for smooth surfaces. For rough surfaces, iodine fumes can be blown onto a surface.

CAN-DO TASK
Level   3   2   **1**

I can take a set of fingerprints.

Taking fingerprints

The police take fingerprints from people using ink pads, or by scanning fingers using a computer. These methods make a record of a person's fingerprints. After a burglary, the police might take fingerprints from all the innocent people who live in the house. They do this to eliminate them from the inquiry.

Why are fingerprints useful?

No two people have the same fingerprints – even identical twins. Your fingerprint pattern does not change during your life.

Fingerprints are matched using patterns. The main ones are: an arch, a loop and a whorl. For a good match between two fingerprints, 16 identical patterns need to be spotted.

What is this policeman using to take fingerprints?

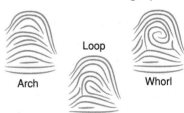

Arch   Loop   Whorl

Main fingerprint patterns.

? QUESTIONS

5 How could you remove fingerprints?

6 What are the **three** main patterns in fingerprints?

7 How many identical patterns need to be seen for fingerprints to match?

CHALLENGE QUESTION:

8 Suggest advantages of the police electronically scanning fingerprints.

---

key words: arch   eliminate   fingerprint   loop   whorl

Blood

Blood and other cells can be left at crime scenes. A blood sample can help to identify someone. The sample needs to be collected and sent away to be tested.

Blood is a mixture of cells that float about in a liquid called plasma. It contains:

♦ red cells which carry oxygen

♦ white cells which fight infections

♦ platelets which are bits of cells that block wounds.

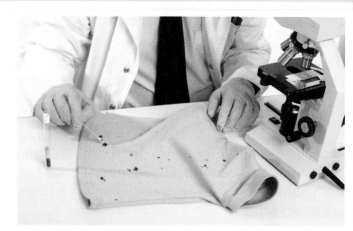

What can be learnt from this blood sample?

Blood groups

There are four different blood groups, A, B, AB and O.

The difference between blood groups is due to chemicals attached to every red blood cell.

Blood can also carry another chemical called the rhesus factor. 85% of people have this so their blood is called positive. Blood without this chemical is called negative.

The most common blood group in the UK is O positive and the rarest is AB negative, which only 1% of people have.

Blood testing can help to convict, or be used to prove someone is innocent. As many people have the same blood group this is not enough to prove if a person actually committed a crime.

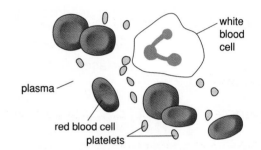

Blood is made up of a mixture of cells, platelets and plasma.

Country	Blood group			
	O	A	B	AB
UK	47	42	8	3
Egypt	33	36	24	8
India	37	22	33	7
Japan	17	33	32	18
Jamaica	43	27	25	5

The main blood groups in some countries.

? QUESTIONS

9 What do red blood cells do?

10 What are the four blood groups?

11 Which blood group is the most common in the UK?

CHALLENGE QUESTION:

12 Draw a bar chart to show blood groups in the UK.

key words: blood group   cell   innocent   plasma

Chromatography

If you have done Item C10 Sorting out you will know about chromatography. It is used to separate the colours in dyes like inks.

It can be used to find out which type of ink was used in a letter or on a bank cheque. Testing the inks can show if a document has been altered, or to match ink to the pen used to write it.

To make a chromatogram, a sample of the ink needs to be dissolved. Then a drop of the sample is put onto filter paper.

A solvent like water is used to separate the dyes.

Chromatography is also used to separate blood and identify chemicals in it, for example drugs like cocaine.

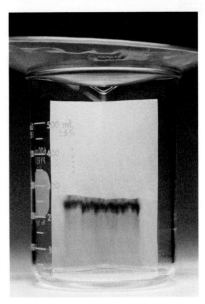

Chromatography is used to separate the colours in ink. Why is this good evidence?

DNA

Every cell in you contains DNA (except for red blood cells).

DNA is a chemical that carries your genetic code. You inherit DNA from your parents – some from your mother and some from your father. Identical twins have the same DNA, but everyone else has DNA that is unique.

If any body cells are found at a crime scene, the DNA can be identified. This is called a DNA fingerprint.

A criminal convicted of a serious crime has to give a DNA sample. This is stored on a national DNA database. Many countries do this. The databases can be used to quickly find out if anyone matches a DNA sample found at a crime scene. DNA evidence is only useful in court if the sample can be shown to be complete and not contaminated.

Some people are concerned that their DNA fingerprint might still be on a database even if they are cleared of a crime.

CAN-DO TASK

Level   3   **2**   1

I can make a chromatogram.

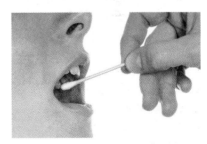

Cheek cells are used to collect a DNA sample. Why is DNA useful evidence?

? QUESTIONS

13 How can an ink sample be removed from a bank cheque?

14 What is DNA?

15 When is DNA evidence not useful in court?

CHALLENGE QUESTION:

16 How can chromatography be used to find out if a cheque has been altered?

key words: chromatogram   chromatography   DNA   DNA fingerprint   unique

PROCESSING DATA
Comparing blood groups

The four main blood groups are O, A, B and AB.

Blood can also be positive or negative.

It is important to know which blood group you are in case you ever need to be given blood.

Being given the wrong type of blood could kill you.

The National Health Service relies on people giving blood. These people are called blood donors. They give about 0.5 litres at each visit.

The chart shows the number of people in the UK with each blood group.

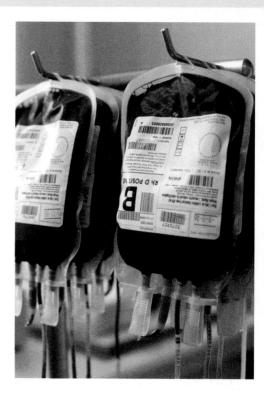

Blood group	Percentage of the population
O positive	37
O negative	7
A positive	35
A positive	7
B positive	8
B negative	2
AB positive	3
AB negative	1

YOUR TASK

1 Draw a bar chart to show these results.
- What will go on the bottom axis?
- What will go on the side axis?
- What scale will you use?
- What title will you put on your chart?

2 Work out the total amount for each blood group by adding the positive and negative results together.

3 Now draw another bar chart to show this.

Maths Skills

Level 3 2 **①**

Select information from tables and charts.

Maths Skills

Level 3 **②** 1

Extract and interpret information from tables.

Maths Skills

Level **③** 2 1

Carry out simple calculations.

C11 CHECKLIST

I have learnt that...

✓ anyone present at a crime scene leaves evidence.

✓ evidence needs to be collected, bagged and labelled.

✓ fingerprints are left on surfaces because oils from the skin are left behind.

✓ tyre and shoe prints are made on soft surfaces.

✓ dusting with powder can make fingerprints show up.

✓ fingerprints can be removed from surfaces.

✓ innocent people have their fingerprints taken to eliminate them from inquiries.

✓ blood contains red cells, white cells, platelets and plasma.

✓ the four blood groups are O, A, B, and AB.

✓ chromatography can be used to separate colours in inks.

✓ DNA is inherited from parents.

✓ only identical twins have identical DNA and everyone else has unique DNA.

I can ...

✓ take a set of fingerprints
➡CAN-DO TASK Level ①.

✓ recognise an arch, loop and whorl in a fingerprint.

✓ explain why crime scene investigators (CSIs) need to wear special clothing.

✓ make a chromatogram
➡CAN-DO TASK Level ②.

✓ understand how the results for separating colours can be used for identification.

✓ interpret crime scene data given to me.

Fuels

I go to road traffic accidents and fires, and rescue people from rivers and floods. I visit homes and fit smoke detectors and carbon monoxide detectors. I also inspect public buildings like schools to check fire alarms and extinguishers.

In my job, I need to know about how different fuels burn and how to put them out. I have to use rescue equipment like breathing apparatus and metal cutters.

Crude oil

Crude oil is a dark, sticky and toxic liquid. It is a fossil fuel that has formed underground over millions of years. Oil is extracted from the ground by drilling into the rock that contains it. Crude oil is mainly a mixture of different length chains of hydrocarbons. Hydrocarbons contain only two elements, hydrogen and carbon. The number of carbons a hydrocarbon has is used to sort the fuels into different types.

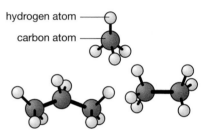

hydrogen atom

carbon atom

Simple hydrocarbons.

Using fuels

Crude oil can be split up into different fuels.

Boiling point is linked to the size of the hydrocarbons. The smaller the hydrocarbon chains are, the lower the boiling point and the easier they are to set alight.

Fraction	Boiling point in °C	Uses
petroleum gases like propane and butane	less than 40	bottled gas for camping or portable heaters
petrol	40–175	fuel for cars
kerosene	175–260	fuel for jet engines
diesel	260–330	fuel for cars, lorries, trains
lubricating oil and waxes	330–490	lubricating oils to protect engines, waxes and polish
bitumen and tar	more than 500	to make roads

? QUESTIONS

1 What is crude oil like?

2 Which elements are in hydrocarbons?

3 What is the boiling point range of jet engine fuel?

CHALLENGE QUESTION:

4 Draw a bar chart to show the range of boiling points of the different fuels.

key words: boiling point   crude oil   hydrocarbon   toxic

Separating crude oil

Crude oil is not very useful until it is split up into different fuels. It is separated in an oil refinery by fractional distillation.

The crude oil is heated. This turns the different hydrocarbons into gases. As the gases rise up the tower, they cool and condense into different fuels.

Different fuels

The diagram shows the different fuels we get from crude oil. At the top of the tower petroleum gases like butane and propane are made. These gases contain few carbons.

The diagram shows this as C_1 to C_4. This means these gases are a mixture of hydrocarbons with only 1 to 4 carbons in them. The number of carbons in the different fuels increases down the tower.

fractional distillation column

fractions decreasing in density and boiling point

fractions increasing in density and boiling point

crude oil mixture is added

it is heated and evaporates

< 40°C C_1 to C_4 gases	bottled gas
40–175°C C_5 to C_{10} naphtha	petrol and chemicals for synthesis
175–260°C C_{11} to C_{14} kerosene	jet fuel, paraffin for lighting and heating
260–330°C C_{15} to C_{20} diesel	diesel fuels
up to 490°C C_{20} to C_{70} heavy oil and lubricants	lubricating oils, waxes, polishes
up to 580°C	fuels for ships, factories and central heating
over 580°C	bitumen for roads and roofing

Fractional distillation of crude oil.

Burning fuels

Most families have a car that uses fuel for transport. But fuels are also used for heating and making electricity.

Plastics

Plastics are also made from small molecules in crude oil called monomers. Lots of monomers join together to make a long-chain polymer.

People are worried that if we continue to burn oil, it will run out and we will no longer have any to make plastics.

? QUESTIONS

5 How is crude oil separated?

6 What are monomers?

7 What is made by burning fuels in power stations?

CHALLENGE QUESTION:

8 Why do small hydrocarbons rise higher up the tower in fractional distillation?

key words: condense   fractional distillation   fuel   monomer   polymer

Measuring the energy in a fuel

You can compare how much energy is in a fuel by burning it.

Do this by using a fuel to heat water and measuring the temperature rise of the water. This only works if the test is fair. To compare the energy in liquid fuels:

♦ use the same sized container called a calorimeter

♦ heat the same amount of water

♦ start with the water at the same temperature

♦ burn the fuel for the same amount of time

♦ have the flame the same size

♦ have the flame the same distance from the container.

To compare solid fuels, hold the fuel in tongs, set fire to it, and hold it under the container of water.

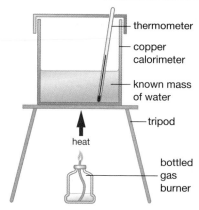

thermometer

copper calorimeter

known mass of water

tripod

heat

bottled gas burner

Burning a liquid fuel.

Burning

All fuels need oxygen to burn. You might have seen this equation before:

fuel + oxygen → carbon dioxide + water

When a fuel gets enough oxygen, it burns cleanly with a blue flame. If a fuel does not get enough oxygen, it can make a poisonous gas called carbon monoxide. A sign of this is a yellow sooty flame.

fuel + little oxygen → carbon monoxide + soot + water

What can a yellow sooty flame be a sign of?

Keeping safe

Carbon monoxide is called the silent killer. You cannot see it, smell it or taste it but it kills when people breathe it in. Getting boilers, cookers and fires in your home serviced every year and fitting a carbon monoxide detector can save your life.

CAN-DO TASK

Level   3   **2**   1

I can make a poster to warn about the dangers of carbon monoxide poisoning.

How can this carbon monoxide alarm save your life?

❓ QUESTIONS

9 State **three** ways to make sure tests to compare burning solid fuels are fair.

10 When is carbon dioxide made?

11 State **two** ways to protect yourself from carbon monoxide poisoning.

CHALLENGE QUESTION:

12 Describe the difference between burning in a lot and in a little oxygen.

key words: carbon monoxide   energy   fair test   oxygen

Petrol or diesel cars?

Car	Diesel VW Golf S 1.6 TDI	Petrol VW Golf S 1.2 TSI
driving in town (miles per litre)	10.9	8.8
all driving (miles per litre)	13.8	10.9
engine emissions (g/kg)	188	118
engine noise level (dB)	69	57
acceleration 0–60 (s)	12.9	10.9
current price new (£)	17 850	16 715

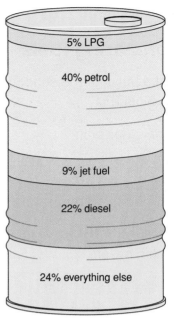

5% LPG

40% petrol

9% jet fuel

22% diesel

24% everything else

This is what we get from a barrel of oil.

I think petrol cars are best. You get better acceleration and a faster top speed. Cars need servicing more often. Petrol is slightly cheaper than diesel.

I think diesel cars are best. They do more miles per litre than petrol. They only need servicing every 10 000 miles but they cost more than a petrol car. Diesel engines are designed to last for over 100 000 miles.

? QUESTIONS

13 How many miles per litre do you get from the diesel car when driving in town?

14 Which car has most engine noise and by how much?

15 Which car accelerates fastest?

CHALLENGE QUESTION:

16 State **one** disadvantage and **three** advantages of each type of car.

key words: acceleration diesel petrol

REVIEWING THE DATA

Comparing fuels

Nadia burnt some solid fuels to see which heated water the most.

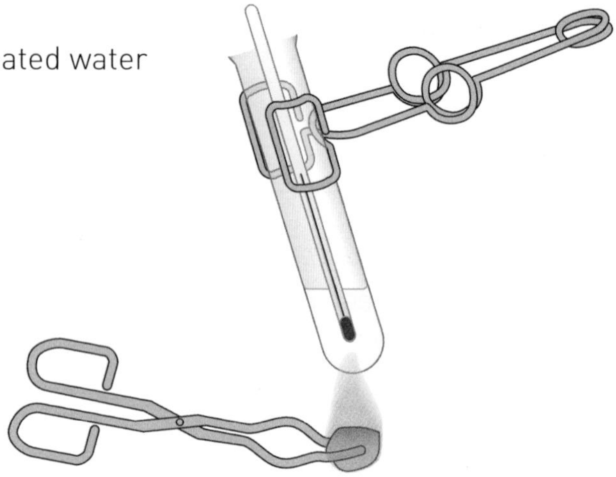

Here is her plan:

1 Put 2 cm depth of fresh water in a tube.

2 Take the temperature of the water.

3 Use 1 g of each solid. Hold it with a pin or tongs.

4 Use a flame to set it on fire.

5 Hold it under the tube of water until it burns out.

6 Take the temperature of the water.

7 Do this with the other fuels, but start with fresh water each time.

Here is Nadia's results table.

Fuel	Crisps	Marshmallow	Pasta
end temp in °C	35	48	34
start temp in °C	23	25	21
rise in temp °C			

YOUR TASK

1 Work out the temperature rise for each food.
2 Which fuel gave out the most energy?
3 What did Nadia do to make this a fair test?
4 What could Nadia have added to her plan to make the method a fairer test?
5 How could Nadia have improved her results?

Maths Skills

Level 3 2 **1**

Select information from tables.

Maths Skills

Level **3** 2 1

Carry out simple calculations.

C12 CHECKLIST

I have learnt that...

- ✓ crude oil is a dark, toxic, sticky liquid.

- ✓ crude oil is a mixture that is separated into more useful parts at an oil refinery.

- ✓ petroleum gases, petrol and diesel come from crude oil.

- ✓ crude oil is made mainly of hydrocarbons of different lengths.

- ✓ fuels with fewer carbons light more easily, and this is linked to their uses.

- ✓ fuels are used for transport, heating and making electricity in power stations.

- ✓ carbon monoxide is a poisonous, colourless gas with no smell or taste.

- ✓ people can choose which fuel to use.

- ✓ plastics are made from lots of small monomers which join up into a long-chain polymer.

I can ...

- ✓ give a use for petroleum gases, petrol, kerosene, diesel.

- ✓ label the apparatus used to find the energy in a fuel.

- ✓ interpret data to find which fuel is best when the same amount burns.

- ✓ make a poster to warn people about the dangers of carbon monoxide poisoning ⟹CAN-DO TASK Level ②.

- ✓ interpret information on carbon monoxide poisoning.

- ✓ give an advantage and a disadvantage of using petrol or diesel in cars.

What is added to our food?

I am a dietician

I advise people about healthy eating. Some people are not eating a balanced diet, which leads to health problems like high blood pressure, diabetes and obesity. I also work with people who have food allergies. These seem to be on the increase. When I visit people I often look in their fridges and freezers.

For my job I need to know about how different food types affect the body. I need to explain how to read labels. This is really important for people with allergies.

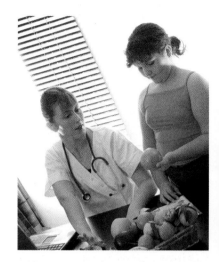

Food additives

Some foods contain chemicals added by the people who make it. These are called additives.

Additives that have passed a safety test are given an E number.

There are people who are allergic to food additives. They get a rash or swelling. Some reactions are so severe people need to inject a drug called adrenaline. They inject the drug using an EpiPen.

Tests can be done to find out which additives people are allergic to.

E number codes	What it is for
E100–E199	colouring
E200–E299	preservatives
E300–E399	antioxidants
E400–E499	stabilisers
E600–E699	flavouring

TOMATO SAUCE
Ingredients: Wheatflour, Vegetable Oil with Antioxidants (E320, E321), Cheese & Tomato Flavour [Flavour Enhancer (621), Flavouring, Colours (E102, E110, E124, 164), Acidity Regulators (E262, E331), Acetic Acid, Citric Acid, Artificial Sweetener (Saccharin)], Maltodextrin, Salt, Tomato, Sweetcorn, Chives, Preservative (E220).
Sachet: Tomato Sauce.

Additives are shown on food labels. Why is it important that food allergy sufferers read the information carefully?

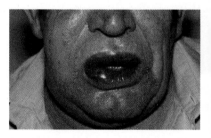

Allergic reactions can cause swelling of the lips, mouth and throat. Why can they be a serious threat?

? QUESTIONS

1 What are food additives?

2 What is E310 used as?

3 If someone has a severe allergic reaction to food additives or other things, what should they carry?

CHALLENGE QUESTION:

4 E numbers are tested, so why do some people have allergic reactions?

160

key words: allergic   additive   E number   EpiPen

Antioxidants

Oxygen from the air can change the taste of food. If an apple is sliced up, the cut cells slowly turn brown. Chemicals in the cut cells react with oxygen. Cooks can use an antioxidant to stop this browning.

Antioxidants are chemicals that stop the effects of oxygen. When you eat them, they protect cells in your body. Many fruits have natural antioxidants in them. Examples are limes, lemons, apples, tomatoes, carrots, blackberries and grapes.

All these foods contain natural antioxidants. Why are they good for us?

Preserving food

Putting antioxidants into foods is one way of preserving food.

Other ways include:
♦ cooling or freezing
♦ smoking or drying
♦ packaging in air-tight tins, jars or plastic
♦ vacuum packing.

All these ways stop oxygen and bacteria getting into food. Crisps need to be kept airtight and dry. Moisture makes them soggy and oxygen changes the taste. Crisp packets are filled with dry nitrogen gas to stop this.

Many people make jam. To stop oxygen getting in when the lid is put on, the jam needs to be hot enough to steam. When the steam condenses, the small space between the jam and lid forms a vacuum.

The lid is often pulled in. Some jars you buy use this idea so you can test the food is airtight.

Why is the top of this jar airtight?

? QUESTIONS

5 What can oxygen gas do to food?

6 Give **three** examples of foods that contain natural antioxidants.

7 Why are crisp packets filled with dry nitrogen gas?

CHALLENGE QUESTION:

8 Apples contain natural antioxidants, so why do cut apples turn brown?

---

key words: antioxidant   bacteria   oxygen   preserve

Vitamins

Your body needs vitamins to stay healthy. You only need vitamins in very small amounts. If you eat a balanced diet, you should get all the different vitamins your body needs.

Vitamins are added to some foods like cereals to make sure you get enough, but some people prefer to make sure by spending money on vitamin tablets.

The different vitamins are given the letters, A, B, C, D and E.

You can get vitamin D by just being in the sun. Sunlight lets your body make it. All the other vitamins have to be eaten.

This plate shows the amounts of different food types needed for a balanced diet. Which foods contain a lot of vitamin C?

Vitamin C

Vitamin C is found in fruit and vegetables. Vitamin C keeps skin and gums healthy and helps makes wounds heal faster.

A lack of vitamin C causes a disease called scurvy. Sailors in olden days often suffered from scurvy, but eating a lime every day prevented it.

Vitamin C can be destroyed when food is boiled. To reduce vitamin C loss, vegetables can be steamed or microwaved and fruit can be eaten raw.

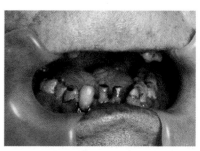

Scurvy can lead to swollen, bleeding gums. Which vitamin is lacking in scurvy sufferers?

Sugar

Sugar is a natural sweetener and a preservative. Sugar we buy in bags is made from sugar cane or sugar beet.

Sugar is in many foods we buy, like cakes, bread and fizzy drinks. We need sugar for energy. Too much sugar can be harmful to health increasing obesity and making you tired.

Many slimming foods and diet drinks contain artificial sweeteners, but these might also cause health problems.

? QUESTIONS

9 Why does your body need vitamins?

10 Why are vitamins added to some foods?

11 State **two** uses of sugar.

CHALLENGE QUESTION:

12 Why do we need sugar, and why is too much harmful?

key words: artificial sweetener   balanced diet   sugar   vitamin

Salt and health

Salt is used in the food industry as a flavouring and as a preservative. Salt brings out the flavours in food and helps to stop food going off. Many processed foods like sauces, ready meals and snack food contain a lot of salt.

In the UK the recommended salt intake for adults is 6 g a day. On average, the UK population take in 9 g a day.

Eating too much salt is linked to high blood pressure and heart attacks. It can also make asthma attacks worse.

Food traffic light labels

The government has introduced a colour code system to show how much salt, fats and sugar are in food.

If the label is green it means low, amber is medium and red is high.

How do we obtain salt?

Salt is a chemical called sodium chloride. Every litre of sea-water contains about 35 g of salt.

In hot countries, sea-water can be collected in shallow lakes and left so the Sun evaporates the water. This leaves the salt behind.

Salt deposits can be found underground. These can be dug out of the ground by mining or quarrying. Some salt deposits are found as rock salt. Rock salt is mainly used for spreading onto roads in winter.

When salt is obtained from the sea or from mines, it can be blown onto the land. If the salt gets into soil it can stop plants and crops growing. Obtaining salt can be dusty and noisy and increase the amount of lorries on roads.

One eclair provides...
cal 218 / fat 16.0g / sat fat 8.2g / salt 0.3g / total sugars 10.5g

Which food types are high in an eclair?

Getting salt from the sea in Spain.

? QUESTIONS

13 Give **two** uses of salt in the food industry.

14 What health problems can come from eating too much salt?

15 What problems are caused by salt extraction?

CHALLENGE QUESTION:

16 Suggest why the traffic light labelling system has been introduced.

key words: evaporate   mining   quarrying   salt

PATTERNS IN THE DATA

How does cooking affect vitamin C?

Jaz and Chris know that vitamin C is tested using a chemical called DCPIP. It is a blue solution.

When it reacts with vitamin C it loses its colour.

Jaz and Chris heated 10 cm³ of apple juice.

After every 10 °C rise they took out 1 cm³ with a pipette and put it in a test tube.

They added DCPIP drop by drop and counted how many drops were needed before the solution turned colourless.

Here are their results.

Temperature in °C	Drops (1st)	Drops (2nd)	Mean
20	8	12	
30	18	20	
40	22	26	
50	26	28	
60	28	27	

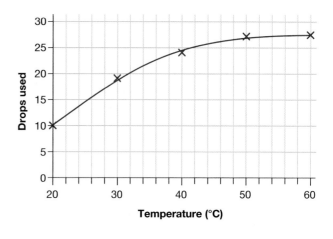

YOUR TASK

1 Work out the mean values.
2 What was the temperature range?
3 What happens to the number of drops used when the temperature goes up?
4 What trend is shown by the data?
5 What happens to vitamin C when apple juice is cooked?

Maths Skills

Level 3 **2** 1

Extract and interpret information from tables and graphs.

Maths Skills

Level **3** 2 1

Calculate arithmetical means.

C13 CHECKLIST

I have learnt that...

✓ some foods contain chemicals called additives.

✓ additives include antioxidants, flavour enhancers and food colours.

✓ tested food additives are given an E number.

✓ the E number shows what the additive does.

✓ oxygen from the air can make food go bad.

✓ antioxidants stop oxygen harming food.

✓ vitamins are added to some foods.

✓ vitamins are needed to keep us healthy.

✓ sugar is a natural sweetener.

✓ too much sugar can be harmful to health.

✓ diet drinks and slimming foods contain artificial sweeteners.

✓ salt is used for flavouring and as a preservative.

✓ salt is obtained from sea-water or underground deposits.

✓ eating too much salt causes health problems.

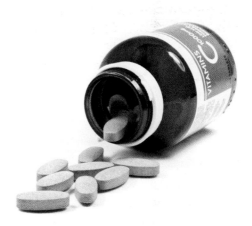

I can ...

✓ interpret information given to me about food additives.

✓ understand that antioxidants preserve food by stopping the effects of oxygen.

✓ interpret results for testing antioxidants.

✓ compare information about recommended amounts of vitamins from data given to me.

✓ test foods for vitamin C
➡ CAN-DO TASK Level ③.

PHYSICS

Getting the message

I am a pop singer

I use wireless technology when I perform. The radio microphone is an advantage. I can dance around the stage while I'm singing. I do not have to stay in one place or have a long trailing lead. I can even go down into the audience.

When I'm on tour, I have my laptop and mobile phone with me. They also use wireless technology, which means that I can use them almost anywhere too. It doesn't matter where I am, I can keep in touch with family, friends and fans.

Wireless technology

Microphones, laptops and mobile phones communicate using radio waves. Radio waves travel at the speed of light (300 000 km/s). This means messages can be sent very quickly. Some signals are sent to a satellite and back to Earth. They travel over 70 000 km in less than ¼ second.

Signals can be sent from Earth to a satellite and back very quickly.

Sending messages

Messages can be sent in many ways. Sometimes people write messages or pass them on by word of mouth. Messages sent by smoke signals and signalling lamps need a code. These messages must be sent carefully to avoid errors.

Some computer mice communicate using infrared radiation. Infrared radiation belongs to the same family of waves as light and radio waves. Most remote control handsets use infrared radiation.

> **Remember,** sound travels at a speed of about 340 m/s. Radio waves travel at the speed of light. ⚠

? QUESTIONS

1 Which of these uses wireless technology? electric drill, microwave oven, satnav.

2 What are the advantages of using wireless technology?

CHALLENGE QUESTION:

3 James and Sheena are standing at each end of a 100 m race track. They have two-way radios. Sheena shouts to James while her radio is on. Why does James hear the message twice?

key words: infrared   radio   satellite   wireless

On the mobile

Mobile phones are a very convenient way of keeping in touch with home and with friends. Although it is not always possible to get a signal, most of the country is covered by most mobile networks. Some networks share their aerials. This cuts down cost and the number of masts.

Mobile phones use microwaves as their signal. Microwaves also travel at the speed of light. Microwaves have quite a long range, but their signal travels in a straight line. This means the aerials have to be in 'line of sight'.

Why do mobile phone masts have to be in 'line of sight'?

Line of sight

For aerials to be in line of sight, they must be mounted very high up or close together.

This stops buildings and hills from getting in the way of the signal. Many mobile phone masts are disguised because people think they spoil the scenery.

Mobile danger

Some scientists think that using mobile phones too much can be harmful. Young people could be harmed more because their bodies have not fully developed.

Many people are worried that the microwave radiation from phone masts can be dangerous. They think it may even cause cancer. To be on the safe side, young people are advised to text or use hands-free kits.

Why are young poeple advised to text on their mobiles?

> **Remember,** mobile phones do not cook the brain! ⚠

❓ QUESTIONS

4 What is the speed of a microwave signal?

5 Suggest **one** way of reducing any danger from mobile phones.

CHALLENGE QUESTION:

6 A mobile phone network wants to put up a mast in the centre of town near to a school. Suggest **one** reason why they want to put the mast there. Suggest **one** reason why some people do not want the mast there.

key words: aerial   line of sight   microwave   network

Waving

When you see a Mexican wave at a football match, you can see the spectators move up and down as the wave moves around the stadium.

Light, infrared, microwaves and radio waves are all the same type of wave. They are transverse waves.

In a transverse wave, the particles vibrate in one direction. The wave moves at right angles to them.

Waves have the following properties:

♦ Amplitude is the maximum distance a particle moves from its rest position.

♦ Wavelength is the distance between one point on a wave and the next similar point.

♦ Frequency is the number of complete waves passing a point in one second. It is measured in hertz (Hz).

When you throw a stone into water, waves spread out and the water moves up and down. Energy from this movement moves outwards with the waves, but the water itself does not move outwards.

Are these water waves transverse waves?

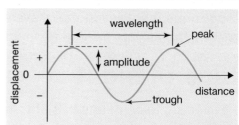
Properties of a wave.

Analogue signals

In the picture on the right, a microphone is connected to an oscilloscope. The trace on the screen represents the note being played. The shape of the wave shows the amplitude and frequency. Both are changing continually and can have any value. This is called an analogue signal.

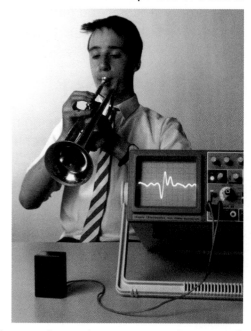
What produces the pattern on the screen?

? QUESTIONS

7 A wave has a frequency of 250 Hz. How many waves pass a point in one second?

8 The energy from a projector bulb is transferred to a screen. Answer true or false to this statement. 'The energy is transferred by the air in the room.'

CHALLENGE QUESTION:

9 Look at the oscilloscope trace above.

a) What does the height of the wave represent?

b) Some parts of the wave are closer together than others. What does this mean?

key words: amplitude   frequency   transverse   wavelength

The digital revolution

Many countries are switching from analogue to digital television. In the UK the government prepared plans for the switch to happen region by region.

Remember that analogue signals can have any value. Digital signals are either on or off. We often represent on as 1 and off as 0. Digital signals are better than analogue signals because they do not show as much interference. This means the picture and sound quality can be much better. You also get:

♦ a much larger choice of programmes
♦ an electronic programme guide
♦ interactive viewing.

Radio programmes can also be transmitted using digital signals and this gives very good sound quality.

Most modern IT equipment relies on digital technology.

Why is digital television being introduced?

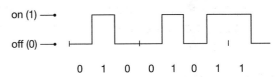

A digital signal can only have one of two values.

Morse code

Morse code uses a system of dots and dashes to represent letters. It is a digital code because there are only two values: on and off.

Until recently, most navies used signalling lamps to communicate between ships in Morse code.

A	B	C	D	E
F	G	H	I	J
K	L	M	N	O
P	Q	R	S	T
U	V	W	X	Y
Z				

Morse code is a digital code.

? QUESTIONS

10 Give **one** advantage of digital television.

11 Why is Morse code a digital signal?

CHALLENGE QUESTION:

12 What does this Morse code message say?

●●● ━●━● ●● ● ━● ━●━● ● / ●● ●●● / ●●━●
●●━ ━● / ━ ━━━ / ━●● ━━━

---

key words: analogue   digital   interference   Morse code

PLANNING TO COLLECT DATA

Sending messages

Messages can be passed on by word of mouth. This is sometimes called Chinese whispers.

Errors can happen when messages are sent.

More errors can happen if the message is coded first because the code may not make sense.

 YOUR TASK

Write a plan to find out how the length of the message and/or the number of people it passes through affects the number of errors made.

Use the answers to the questions to help you write your plan.

1 How many experiments will you need to do to get enough results to draw a graph?

2 How will you make a 'coded' message?

3 How long will the coded message be?

4 How will you record the result of sending the message?

5 How will you decide the number of mistakes made?

6 What graph will you draw?

7 Write or draw out your final plan as a step-by-step list.

P1 CHECKLIST

I have learnt that...

- ✓ messages can be coded and sent quickly using light, radio waves and microwaves.

- ✓ household devices can be controlled using infrared radiation.

- ✓ wireless technology has many advantages.

- ✓ mobile phones use microwaves.

- ✓ there is some concern about the use of mobile phones and phone masts.

- ✓ mobile phone masts must be in line of sight.

- ✓ waves transfer energy through the air but the air does not move with the wave.

- ✓ analogue signals vary continually and digital signals have only two values.

- ✓ Morse code is a digital code.

- ✓ digital signals have many advantages.

- ✓ modern IT equipment relies on digital signals.

> **I can...**
>
> - ✓ interpret information about the siting of mobile phone masts.

Our electricity supply

I am an electrician

I work for an electricity supply company. It's my job to repair the high voltage overhead power lines of the National Grid when they get damaged. Power lines transfer electricity from the power station to the people who use it.

Sometimes, I have to work at the top of electricity pylons. It is safe for me to work there because the electricity has been turned off. If it wasn't, I would be electrocuted. Transformers at the power station increase the voltage. Sometimes it is as high as 400 000V. There are more transformers at the other end of the transmission line. These decrease the voltage to the 230V used in homes and at work.

Making electricity

Some items of electrical equipment use batteries as a source of energy. Others run off mains electricity.

The electricity from a battery is the result of a chemical reaction. Simple batteries can be made using:

♦ two different metal electrodes in acid
♦ a pile of zinc and copper discs separated by filter paper soaked in salt solution.

Different batteries are used in different situations. The choice depends on size as well as the voltage and current needed.

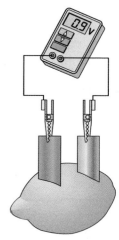

A simple battery made with a lemon.

? QUESTIONS

1 What is the highest voltage used in the National Grid?

2 What is the voltage of electricity in homes?

CHALLENGE QUESTION:

3 Terry tries to make a battery. He connects each lead from a torch bulb to a steel pin and pushes the two pins into a potato. The bulb does not light. Judy does the same experiment. She attaches one lead to a copper pin and the other to a steel pin. She pushes the pins into a lemon. Her bulb lights. Suggest **two** reasons why Terry's bulb does not light.

key words: battery   electrode   National Grid   transformer

Power stations

All power stations need a source of energy.

Many power stations burn fossil fuels to create electricity.

Fossil fuels are formed from the remains of animals and plants that died millions of years ago. This is why they are called fossil fuels.

The main fossil fuels are:

♦ oil   ♦ coal   ♦ natural gas.

In power stations:

1 energy from the burning fuel changes water into steam
2 the steam turns a turbine
3 the turbine turns a generator
4 the generator produces electricity.

At every stage of the process, energy is lost to the surroundings as heat.

Carbon dioxide is produced whenever a fossil fuel burns. This is released into the atmosphere. Carbon dioxide is a greenhouse gas. This means it contributes to global warming.

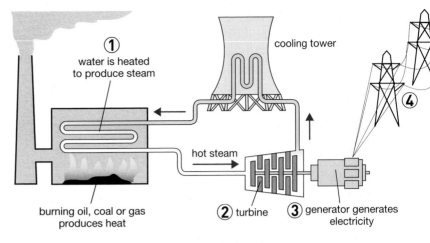

① water is heated to produce steam

cooling tower

hot steam

burning oil, coal or gas produces heat

② turbine

③ generator generates electricity

④

How a power station works.

What is the name for these large towers?

Remember, it is water vapour coming from the large towers of a power station, not smoke. ⚠️

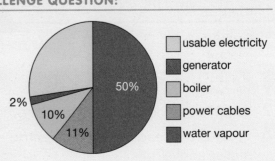

❓ QUESTIONS

4 Why are oil, coal and gas called fossil fuels?

5 What is the job of a turbine in a power station?

CHALLENGE QUESTION:

6 The pie chart shows how much energy is lost in different stages of producing electricity. What percentage of energy is transferred into usable electricity?

- usable electricity
- generator
- boiler
- power cables
- water vapour

50%
2%
10%
11%

key words: generator   global warming   greenhouse gas   turbine

Transformers

A transformer is made by winding two coils of wire onto an iron core. Transformers are used to change the size of a voltage.

Some transformers increase the voltage. These are called step-up transformers. There are more turns of wire on the output coil than the input coil.

Step-up transformers at a power station are very large.

Some transformers decrease the voltage. These are called step-down transformers. There are more turns of wire on the input coil than the output coil.

Some step-down transformers, like those used to charge your mobile phone, can be quite small. Some step-down transformers are very large.

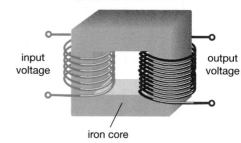

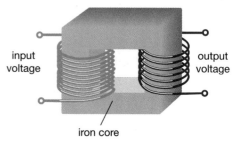

A step-up transformer. Which coil has the most turns of wire on it, the input or the output?

A step-down transformer.

Reading the meter

The electricity we all use at home has to be paid for. The amount we use is recorded on a meter. Most homes have the meter read every 3 or 6 months. The electricity supply company then sends a bill.

When you read an electric meter, the last number is not recorded.

The amount of electricity used is measured in kilowatt-hours. A kilowatt-hour (kWh) is called a *unit* of electricity.

What does the 'kWh' stand for on this electricity meter?

> **Remember,** transformers do not change AC into DC. They only increase or decrease the size of a voltage. ⚠

> **CAN-DO TASK**
> Level 3 **2** 1
>
> I can read a domestic electricity meter.

❓ QUESTIONS

7 What is the job of a transformer?

8 What is the reading on the electric meter above?

CHALLENGE QUESTION:

9 Suggest where you would find a very large step-down transformer.

---

key words: electric meter   iron core   transformer   voltage

Paying for electricity

The cost of electricity is rising. Many people, especially some elderly people, find it difficult to pay their bill.

The amount of electricity we use depends on the power of an appliance and how long it is used for.

Some appliances, like kettles and cookers, have a high power rating. This means they use a lot of electricity. Light bulbs and door bells have a very low power rating which means they use less electricity.

Electricity supply companies show the following information on their bills:

♦ current and last meter readings
♦ units of electricity used and cost per unit
♦ any additional costs, savings and VAT.

Do kettles have a high or low power rating?

Cutting the cost

We can reduce our electricity bills by reducing energy loss from our homes. Most energy is lost through the walls and roof. The rest is lost through the floors, doors and windows.

Energy loss can be reduced by:

♦ curtains, curtain lining, blinds and double glazing
♦ cavity wall insulation   ♦ loft insulation
♦ carpet and underlay   ♦ draught strip around doors.

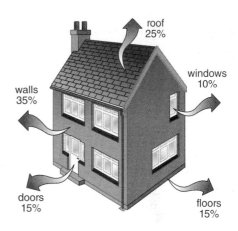

How heat is lost from a house. Which part of the house loses the most energy?

❓ QUESTIONS

10 Look at the electricity bill below. How much does one unit of electricity cost?

Electricity you've used this period					
Meter number **64803 General purpose rate**					
Reading period 4 Mar 11 to 5 Jun 11					
	previous	latest	units	pence	charges
Electricity used	02782	03762	980	13.65	£133.77
VAT @ 5%					£6.68
Total for this period					**£140.45**

11 Suggest **three** ways of reducing energy loss through windows.

CHALLENGE QUESTION:

12 James moves in to an old house that does not have any insulation. He cannot afford to have the house fully insulated. Why should he have cavity wall insulation before double glazing?

---

key words: double glazing   energy   insulation   power

PROCESSING THE DATA
Fruit battery

Two different metals placed in a lemon will produce a voltage.

To find out how the distance between the metals affects the voltage, a strip of zinc and a strip of copper are placed into a lemon. The voltage is recorded. The experiment is repeated with different distances between the metal strips.

The table shows the results.

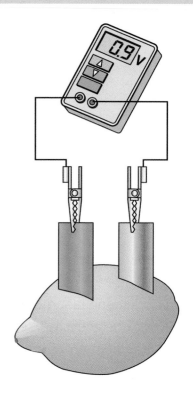

Distance in cm	Voltage in V			
	1st try	2nd try	3rd try	average
2	0.9	0.7	1.1	
3	1.0	1.1	0.9	
4	1.2	0.9	0.9	
5	1.0	1.0	1.3	
6	0.8	1.0	1.2	

Maths Skills

Level 3 2 **1**

Recognise and use numbers to one decimal place.

Maths Skills

Level **3** 2 1

Calculate arithmetical means.

YOUR TASK

1 Calculate the average voltage for each distance of metal strips.
2 Plot a graph of average voltage against distance.
3 Draw a straight line which is the line of best fit.

Maths Skills

Level **3** 2 1

Plot simple line graphs.

P2 CHECKLIST

I have learnt that...

- ⊘ electricity is made by chemical reactions in a battery using two different metals in acid.

- ⊘ crude oil, natural gas and coal are fossil fuels and are the most common energy sources at a power station.

- ⊘ energy is wasted from a power station from the energy source, from the steam, from the turbines and from the generators.

- ⊘ carbon dioxide is a greenhouse gas produced when fuels burn.

- ⊘ greenhouse gases contribute to global warming.

- ⊘ electricity is transmitted around the country at high voltages using overhead power lines in the National Grid.

- ⊘ transformers are used to increase and decrease voltages.

- ⊘ transformers consist of an iron core and two coils of wire.

- ⊘ we pay for electricity by the unit.

- ⊘ electricity bills can be reduced if a home is well insulated.

I can...

- ⊘ read a domestic electricity meter ➠ CAN-DO TASK Level ②.

- ⊘ interpret data on a domestic electricity bill.

- ⊘ interpret data about different ways to save energy.

Attractive forces

I am a radiologist

I work in a hospital in the MRI scanning department. MRI stands for magnetic resonance imaging. The MRI machine uses a very strong magnetic field (up to 40 000 times more powerful than the Earth's magnetic field).

An MRI scanner is the best way to see inside a body without using surgery. It is used to diagnose such things as multiple sclerosis, brain tumours, torn ligaments, cancers and strokes.

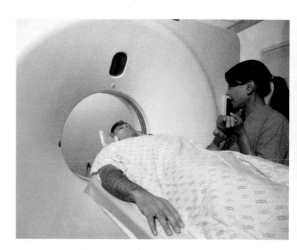

Simple magnets

Iron and steel are magnetic. This means they are attracted to a magnet.

Iron and steel pins can be magnetised. This means they can be made into magnets.

To make a pin into a magnet, stroke it along its length with a magnet. Do this several times but always in the same direction.

One end of the magnet is the north pole and the other end is the south pole.

If two north poles, or two south poles are brought close together, they repel (move apart).

If a north pole and a south pole are brought close together, they attract.

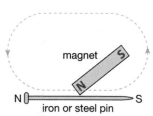

A simple way to make a magnet.

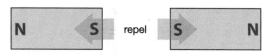
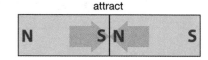

Like poles repel and unlike poles attract.

QUESTIONS

1 What are the ends of a magnet called?

2 How can you magnetise a steel knitting needle?

CHALLENGE QUESTION:

3 The ends of two pieces of steel are brought together and they repel. What does this tell you about the pieces of steel?

key words: magnet   MRI scanner   pole   repel

Magnetic fields

A magnet has a magnetic field around it. You can see the shape of the field using iron filings or a small compass.

The Earth's field

The Earth has a magnetic field around it. A freely swinging magnet will point in a North–South direction. A compass needle points to the magnetic North Pole.

The magnetic North Pole is close to the geographic North Pole. This means that walkers and explorers can use maps and a compass to help them find their way.

The Earth behaves as if there is a magnet inside it. But, since unlike poles attract, there is a magnetic south pole at the North Pole.

Cosmic rays

Cosmic rays are particles from beyond the Earth's atmosphere that bombard the Earth.

They can be damaging to health and are thought to cause cataracts and increase the risk of cancer.

They also affect the formation of clouds and thunderstorms. Electronic circuits can also be affected.

The Earth's atmosphere stops many of the cosmic rays. The Earth's magnetic field helps to protect us from the rays that pass through the atmosphere. At the North and South Poles, the magnetic field interacts with the cosmic rays. This results in a spectacular light show known as the Northern (or Southern) Lights.

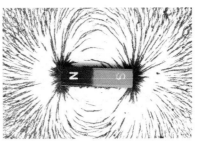

What do these iron filings around the magnet show?

CAN-DO TASK

Level **3** 2 1

I can use a plotting compass to map a magnetic field.

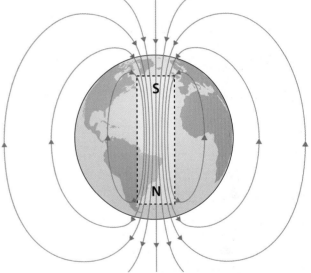

The Earth's magnetic field.

Remember, the Earth behaves as if there is a south pole of a magnet at the North Pole. ⚠

❓ QUESTIONS

4 In which direction does a compass needle point?

5 Write down **two** effects of cosmic rays on Earth.

6 What magnetic pole is inside the Earth close to the geographic South Pole?

CHALLENGE QUESTION:

7 Why are astronauts more likely to suffer from cataracts than airline pilots?

---

key words: compass   cosmic ray   magnetic field   Northern Lights

Magnetic fields due to electric currents

There is a magnetic field around a wire if an electric current is passing through the wire.

When the wire is coiled up, the field is the same as the field due to a bar magnet.

♦ If the number of turns on the coil increases, the magnetic field becomes stronger.
♦ If the current in the coil increases, the magnetic field becomes stronger.

This effect is used in loudspeakers.

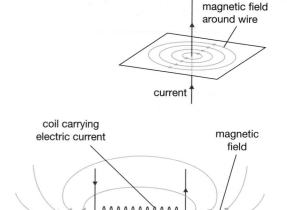

A coiled wire carrying an electric current, resulting in a magnetic field.

Loudspeaker

The loudspeaker consists of a coil attached to a cone.

The coil can vibrate inside a circular magnet.

1 A changing current, (from a radio or CD player, for example) passes through the coil.
2 This produces a changing magnetic field.
3 The coil is attracted and repelled by the magnet.
4 The cone vibrates as the coil moves.
5 This produces sound.

If the current in the coil is larger, the coil vibrates more. This makes the cone vibrate more. This makes the sound louder.

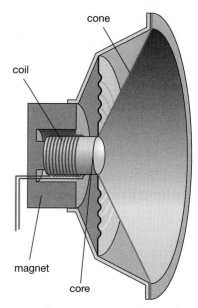

Cross-section of a loudspeaker.

? QUESTIONS

8 What happens to the loudness of sound from a loudspeaker if the current in the coil is reduced?

9 Draw the magnetic field pattern due to a bar magnet.

10 Finish the sentence. 'As the number of turns on a coil of wire increases, the magnetic field becomes ....'

CHALLENGE QUESTION:

11 How does the construction of a loudspeaker allow the coil and cone to vibrate?

key words: cone   coil   core   current   loudspeaker

Electromagnets

Electromagnets are very useful.

♦ They can be used to separate iron and steel from other metals at a scrapyard.

♦ They can be used to move heavy iron or steel objects, such as cars, around.

Electromagnets are made from a coil of wire wrapped around an iron core.

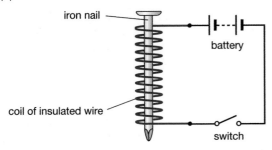

An electromagnet.

How does an electromagnet work?

When a current is passing through the coil, the iron becomes magnetised. It attracts iron and steel objects.

When the DC current is switched off, the iron demagnetises. It stops attracting the iron and steel objects. They fall off.

Iron is a temporary magnet. This is why it loses its magnetism when the current is switched off. Steel is a permanent magnet.

The electromagnet becomes stronger if:

♦ the current in the coil is increased
♦ the number of turns on the coil is increased.

How does the scrap drop from the electromagnet?

? QUESTIONS

12 What type of current is used for an electromagnet?

13 How can the strength of an electromagnet be increased?

14 Write down **one** use for an electromagnet.

CHALLENGE QUESTION:

15 Eric makes an electromagnet by wrapping a coil wire around a steel bar. He tests it by picking up paper clips. It can pick up five. What happens to the paper clips when he switches off the current?

key words: demagnetise   electromagnet   permanent   temporary

REVIEWING THE METHOD

What affects the loudness of a loudspeaker?

Sef connects a signal generator to a loudspeaker.

He measures the output from the signal generator with a voltmeter.

He connects a microphone to an oscilloscope and holds the microphone in front of the loudspeaker.

He records the output voltage from the signal generator and the height of the trace on the oscilloscope.

The table shows his results.

Output voltage in V	Height of oscilloscope trace in mm
0	5
2	20
4	16
6	45
8	43
10	75

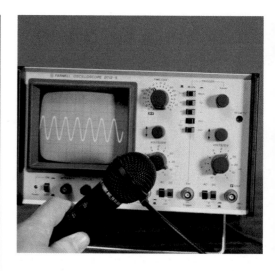

✒ YOUR TASK

1 Look carefully at how Sef collected the data and the results of his investigation.

2 Why do you think the results are erratic?

3 How could he improve his experimental method?

4 How could he make sure his results are as precise as possible?

Maths Skills

Level   3   **2**   1

Extract and interpret information from tables.

P3 CHECKLIST

I have learnt that...

- ✓ iron and steel are magnetic materials.

- ✓ magnets attract magnetic materials.

- ✓ like poles repel and unlike poles attract.

- ✓ the Earth has a magnetic field around it and that a freely swinging magnet will rest in a N–S direction.

- ✓ the Earth's magnetic field protects us from cosmic rays.

- ✓ the Northern Lights are a result of the cosmic rays and magnetic field interacting.

- ✓ a wire with a current passing through it behaves like a magnet.

- ✓ increasing the current or number of turns increases the field in a coil.

- ✓ the core of an electromagnet must be made of iron, not steel.

- ✓ iron is a temporary magnet.

- ✓ electromagnets are used for MRI scanners, sorting scrap metal, lifting heavy weights.

I can...

- ✓ use a plotting compass to map a magnetic field
  ➡ **CAN-DO TASK Level** ③.

- ✓ magnetise a pin.

- ✓ interpret information about the effect of cosmic rays on Earth.

- ✓ label the parts of a loudspeaker.

- ✓ construct an electromagnet.

Pushes and pulls

I am a member of the Red Devils display team. When I jump out of our plane, 3000 metres above the ground, gravity pulls me towards the Earth. I have weight because of this gravitational force.

Another force acting on me is drag (also called air resistance). This acts upwards and works against gravity. When the air resistance is equal to my weight, I am falling at 54 m/s, this is my maximum speed and I cannot go any faster.

Air resistance is affected by my area moving through the air. When I open my parachute I fall at a maximum speed of 4.5 m/s.

Remember, a free-fall parachutist does not go up when the parachute opens, his speed suddenly decreases.

Forces

Forces can:

♦ push ♦ pull ♦ twist ♦ bend.

Any object will either remain still or move at a steady speed unless a force acts on it. For example, a car moves along a road at a constant speed because the thrust from the engine equals the friction from the road and air. These forces cancel out. If the driver takes his foot off the accelerator, the thrust from the engine is less. The frictional forces are larger than the thrust. The car slows down.

Forces are measured using a newton meter. The unit of force is the newton (N).

CAN-DO TASK

Level **3** 2 1

I can measure time accurately.

CAN-DO TASK

Level 3 **2** 1

I can use a newton meter to measure force.

? QUESTIONS

1 What is the highest speed a free-fall parachutist can reach?

2 What happens to the speed of a car if the thrust is larger than the frictional forces?

CHALLENGE QUESTION:

3 Why does a free-fall parachutist slow down when they open their parachute?

key words: drag friction newton newton meter thrust

Bungee!

Imagine jumping off a bridge more than 150 m above a river. You are attached to the bridge by an elastic rope. More than 50 000 people have done so, safely.

The jumper is attracted towards the Earth by gravity. His weight is pulling him down. His speed increases. During his fall, the rope reaches its natural length. The weight of the jumper starts to stretch the rope.

As the rope stretches, it starts to exert a force on the jumper. This force is upwards so the jumper starts to slow down.

When the jumper has stopped, the force from the stretched rope is larger than his weight. He starts to move up again. He continues to move up and down until eventually he stops.

When he is released from the rope, it goes back to its original length. Any material that goes back to its original length is elastic.

Do you think a heavier person using the same length of bungee rope will stretch the rope more or less?

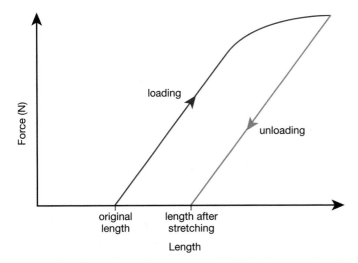

Graph to show how a material that is not elastic behaves if it is stretched too much.

? QUESTIONS

4 Write down the name of **one** elastic material.

5 What happens to an elastic material when a force acts on it?

6 How can you tell that a material is elastic?

CHALLENGE QUESTION:

7 Why is a bungee rope only one fifth of the jump height?

---

key words: elastic   force   gravity   weight

Driving safely

Some accidents happen because drivers have been travelling too fast. Many roads have speed limits to help reduce accidents. Roads by schools and residential roads often have 20 mph speed limits.

Speed can be reduced with the help of:

♦ speed humps ♦ chicanes ♦ speed cameras.

Most roadside speed cameras have now been switched off. The ones used on motorways and other major roads measure average speed over a distance of a mile or two. They take pictures of every car number plate as it passes the first camera and again as it passes the second.

Speed is calculated using the equation:

$$speed = \frac{distance}{time}$$

The distance between the cameras and the time taken is known. The speed is calculated by a computer. If the car is speeding, the driver can be prosecuted.

Crash

If a car does have a crash, it is designed to reduce injury to the driver and passengers.

♦ Crumple zones reduce the force of the impact by changing their shape.
♦ Seat belts reduce the force of the impact by stretching.
♦ Air bags reduce the force of the impact by changing their shape when the person hits them.

What happens when a car goes over a speed bump?

CAN-DO TASK

Level ③ 2 1

I can measure the speed of a moving object.

What has happened to the crumple zones in this crash?

❓ QUESTIONS

8 Write down **two** ways in which speed can be reduced.

9 How does a seat belt help to reduce injury in a crash?

10 What happens to a crumple zone if a car crashes?

CHALLENGE QUESTION:

11 A car travels 220 km along a motorway in 2 hours. What is its average speed?

key words: airbag chicane crumple zone speed

Space forces

On July 16 1969, a Saturn V rocket was launched from the Kennedy Space Centre in Florida. Four days later, the Eagle lunar module landed on the Moon's surface.

The Saturn V rocket is still the largest rocket used to launch a spacecraft. It stood over 100 m tall. Its mass was over 3 million kg (that's the same as 200 family cars).

A very large force is needed to put a spacecraft into space. The force comes from exhaust gases being forced out of the bottom of the rocket very quickly.

You can see the same principle using a water rocket. As the water shoots out of the bottle's neck, the rocket lifts off.

How is a rocket's shape suited to a successful launch?

Reusable rockets

The Saturn V had three rocket stages. The first stage lifted the rocket off the launch pad into the Earth's atmosphere. Once all of the fuel in this stage was used up, the rocket parachuted back to Earth. The rocket was lighter. The second stage rocket took over getting everything into space. Once its fuel was used, it also came back to Earth. Rockets that come back to Earth can be reused. Some rockets burn up as they travel through the atmosphere.

The Space Shuttle was a reusable spacecraft. It was used to ferry astronauts and cargo to the International Space Station. After its mission was over, it landed like an aeroplane. The last Space Shuttle flew in 2011.

What provides the force for this water rocket to take off?

? QUESTIONS

12 What causes a rocket to lift off the launch pad?

13 What happens to a rock from space as it travels quickly through the atmosphere?

14 How does a reusable space rocket return safely to Earth?

CHALLENGE QUESTION:

15 Suggest **one** advantage of a reusable spacecraft like the Space Shuttle.

key words: astronaut   atmosphere   rocket   Space Shuttle

INTERPRETING THE DATA

Parachuting

A parachutist jumps from a plane and free falls before opening her parachute.

Her speed is recorded as she falls.

The table shows the results.

Time in s	Speed in m/s
0	0
2	19
4	33
6	43
8	48
10	51
12	52
14	53
16	54
18	54
20	54

 YOUR TASK

1 Plot a graph of the results.

2 Draw a smooth curve line of best fit.

3 What pattern is shown by the data?

4 Use your knowledge of science to explain why the graph is this shape.

Maths Skills

Level **3** 2 1

Plot simple line graphs.

P4 CHECKLIST

I have learnt that...

- ✓ forces can push, pull, twist, bend.

- ✓ unbalanced forces change how an object moves.

- ✓ the unit of force is the newton (N).

- ✓ gravity is a force towards the Earth.

- ✓ falling objects are affected by gravity and air resistance (drag).

- ✓ falling objects reach a maximum speed.

- ✓ elastic objects stretch when a force acts and then return to their original length unless stretched too much.

- ✓ crumple zones, airbags and seatbelts reduce injuries in a crash by reducing forces.

- ✓ rockets are needed to put objects into space.

- ✓ some parts of rockets and spacecraft can be reused but others burn up in the atmosphere.

I can...

- ✓ use a newton meter to measure force ➡ **CAN-DO TASK** Level ②.

- ✓ measure time accurately ➡ **CAN-DO TASK** Level ③.

- ✓ measure the speed of a moving object ➡ **CAN-DO TASK** Level ③.

- ✓ interpret information about traffic calming measures.

Let there be light

I am a lighting technician

My job is to arrange the lights when a stage is being set up before a show and to control the lighting during the show. I get the best view because I operate the deck that controls the lights. I travel all over the world and work with some of the big names in music.

As a lighting technician I need to understand how to mix different coloured lights to get the colours I need.

Coloured lights

The primary colours for light are red, green and blue.

When two primary colours are shone onto a white screen they form the secondary colours.

Secondary colours are yellow, magenta and cyan.

These secondary colours are made up of the two primary colours as shown here.

red	+	green	=	yellow
green	+	blue	=	cyan
blue	+	red	=	magenta

If all three primary colours are shone onto a screen, white light is formed.

On stage, coloured lights are mixed by changing the brightness of each of the colours. This means that by mixing the correct colours, all the other colours can be made.

> **Remember,** the primary colours for art are different to the primary colours in science. Do not get confused.

Which primary colours and which secondary colour are being used here?

? QUESTIONS

1 Which of these is NOT a primary colour for light? Red, yellow, blue.

2 What colour will a white screen appear if it is lit by green and blue lights?

CHALLENGE QUESTION:

3 When you look at a television screen really closely, you can see that the picture is made up of red, blue and green dots. Suggest why.

---

key words: brightness   colour   primary   secondary

Luminous or non-luminous objects

Until 1000 years ago, people believed that vision happened because light comes out of the eye and hits objects outside. This would mean that the eyes are light producers.

This theory has now been proved wrong. We see an object when light from it reaches our eyes.

All objects are luminous or non-luminous.

Luminous objects produce their own light. Stars, flames and light bulbs are luminous.

Non-luminous objects do not produce their own light. We can see non-luminous objects only because they reflect light.

Most things are non-luminous. Your desk and chair for example do not produce their own light.

Why can we see the stars?
Why can we see the Moon?

Coloured stars

When we look at the night sky, most stars appear as a blurry white light. This is because the stars are a long way away and the light from them gets mixed on its way to us. Some may contain a hint of blue or orange.

Not all stars are the same colour. The colour of a star depends on its temperature.

◆ Some stars are as hot as 40 000 °C.
◆ Some stars are only 3000 °C.
◆ Cold stars are red, hot stars are blue.

Why are stars different colours?

3000 °C	6000 °C	10 000 °C	40 000 °C

Scale showing what colours stars are at different temperatures.

? QUESTIONS

4 Name **two** luminous objects.

5 Name **two** non-luminous objects.

6 Our Sun is a yellow star. What is the temperature of our Sun?

CHALLENGE QUESTION:

7 Venus is a planet. It is called the 'morning star'. Why can we see Venus?

key words: luminous   non-luminous   reflect   temperature

Reflection of light

The laser beams from a laser light show are all straight.

The edges of a shadow are sharp and the same shape as the object casting the shadow.

These observations confirm that light travels in straight lines.

Light is reflected from any smooth, shiny surface. It gives a clear reflection. The scientific name for the reflection you see is the image.

Your image in a mirror appears:

◆ the same size

◆ the same way up

◆ the other way round (right hand becomes left).

When light reflects from a mirror, it obeys the law of reflection:

angle of incidence = angle of reflection

Why can we see ourselves in mirrors?

CAN-DO TASK

Level 3 2 **1**

I can write a message in mirror writing.

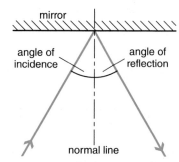

Reflection of light.

Refraction of light

Light changes direction when it passes from one material into another. This is called refraction. It is why a pencil dipped in to a bowl of water appears bent.

As light passes through a transparent block, it is refracted towards the normal as it enters the block. It is refracted away from the normal as it leaves the block.

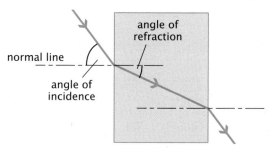

Refraction of light.

❓ QUESTIONS

8 Give **one** example that shows light travels in straight lines.

9 Kevin stands in front of the mirror wearing a t-shirt with writing on. What happens to the writing in his image?

10 How can we see that light has been refracted at a boundary?

CHALLENGE QUESTION:

11 Light strikes a mirror so that the angle between the light and the mirror is 40°. Draw a diagram to show what happens. Write on the values for the angle of incidence and the angle of reflection.

key words: image   reflection   refraction   transparent

Convex lenses

Convex lenses are special shaped blocks of glass or plastic. A light beam converges as it passes through the lens. Convex lenses are sometimes called converging lenses.

converging lens
(shown as a thin blue line)

object ray 1

ray 2

principal axis

F

F

focal point

image

ray 2

intersection of the rays gives top of image

ray 1

Convex lens.

A convex lens can produce an image of an object on a screen.

Convex lenses are used in:

♦ spectacles to correct long sight
♦ cameras

♦ projectors
♦ telescopes
♦ magnifying glasses.

To find the position of an image:

Draw one ray of light from the top of the object so that it passes through the centre of the lens (shown in green).

Draw a second ray of light from the top of the object parallel to the axis. When it reaches the lens, the ray changes direction and passes through the focus (shown in red).

Where the two rays meet is the top of the image.

Optical fibres

When light is going from glass into air, it can be totally reflected inside the glass. This happens if the angle of incidence in the glass is larger than 42°.

Light will travel along a glass fibre by repeated reflections. This is how optic fibre lamps work.

Optical fibres can transmit data very quickly. The data is coded into digital signals. It is then transmitted using a laser at the speed of light. Most of our telephone communications are carried round the country in optical fibres. A single optical fibre cable can carry 40 000 telephone conversations at once.

Why do we use optical fibres for telephone comunications?

? QUESTIONS

12 Write down **two** uses of converging lenses.

13 What happens to a ray of light in glass if its angle of incidence is 60°?

14 At what speed do telephone messages travel along an optical fibre?

CHALLENGE QUESTION:

15 Find out the advantages of transmitting telephone conversations along optical fibres instead of along copper wires.

---

key words: converging   convex   lens   optical fibre

PATTERNS IN THE DATA

Counting images in mirrors

A kaleidoscope works because two mirrors are placed at 60° to each other. The object between the mirrors produces five images.

How many images you can see depends on the angle between the mirrors.

Two mirrors are supported vertically at various angles.

An object is placed between them and the number of images counted.

The table shows the results.

Angle between mirrors	Number of images formed
10	35
20	17
30	11
40	8
60	5
90	3
120	2

Maths Skills

Level **3 2 ①**

Draw bar charts.

YOUR TASK

1 Draw a bar chart of the results.

2 Why is a bar chart better than a line graph?

3 What pattern is shown by the data?

P5 CHECKLIST

I have learnt that...

✓ luminous objects produce their own light and non-luminous reflect light so they can be seen.

✓ light travels in straight lines.

✓ shiny surfaces reflect light to give a clear reflection.

✓ the image in a flat mirror is the same way up and the same size as the object but is the other way round.

✓ light changes direction when it passes from one material into another (refraction).

✓ convex lenses are used for spectacles (long sight), cameras, projectors, telescopes and magnifying glasses.

✓ light can be totally reflected inside water, glass and plastic as it reaches the boundary with air.

✓ light travels along an optical fibre and that messages can be sent in this way with the help of a digital code.

✓ two of the primary colours (red, blue or green) can be mixed to form a secondary colour (yellow, magenta or cyan).

✓ all three primary colours can be mixed to produce white light.

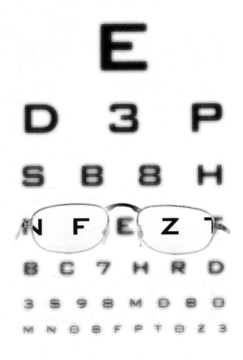

I can...

✓ write a message in mirror writing
➠ **CAN-DO TASK Level** ①.

✓ draw a ray diagram to show how light is reflected from a flat mirror.

✓ complete a ray diagram to show how a convex lens forms an image on a screen.

Final frontier

I am an astronaut

I work on the International Space Station as it orbits the Earth. There are lots of satellites orbiting the Earth. Most of them are unmanned. They do not need the resources we do, like oxygen, food and water.

The view from up here is so clear. We can see things that you cannot see from Earth because dust in the atmosphere and pollution from all the lights on Earth spoil the view.

Searching the skies

People have been studying the sky for thousands of years. The early star gazers gave names to groups of stars. We still use those names today.

In 1609, Galileo made the first telescope. Today, astronomers still use astronomical telescopes to look at the sky.

Space telescopes orbit the Earth and send back pictures. The Hubble Space Telescope has recently discovered another moon orbiting Pluto. Space telescopes have also discovered stars and planets well beyond our Solar System that we cannot see from Earth.

They can see stars, planets, moons, comets, asteroids, meteoroids and artificial satellites.

What does the Hubble Space Telescope do?

The furthest stars are so far away that light from them would take more than 13 billion years to reach Earth.

? QUESTIONS

1 What resources do manned spacecraft need that unmanned ones do not?

2 What do astronomers use to look at the Moon?

CHALLENGE QUESTION:

3 What are the advantages of using a telescope in space instead of one on Earth?

key words: astronaut   astronomer   Space Station   telescope

Solar System

Our Solar System has the Sun at its centre. The Sun is very hot. It provides us with heat and light. The Sun provides so much energy it is possible to burn wood by simply focusing the energy. This is why it is dangerous to look at the Sun.

Why is this wood burning?

The Earth is one of the eight planets that orbit the Sun. The time it takes each of them to orbit depends on their distance from the Sun. The length of the Earth's orbit is 939 million km. The Earth travels at 107 000 km/h around the Sun. That's fast!

Properties of planets

	Mercury	Venus	Earth	Mars	Jupiter	Saturn	Uranus	Neptune
average distance from the Sun (compared to Earth)	0.3871	0.7233	1	1.524	5.203	9.539	19.19	30.06
time to orbit Sun (Earth years)	0.24	0.62	1	1.88	11.86	29.46	84.01	164.79
average diameter (km)	4878	12 104	12 735	6777	138 344	114 628	50 532	49 609
mass of planet (compared to Earth)	0.06	0.82	1	0.11	317.89	95.18	14.53	17.14
time to spin on axis (Earth days)	58.7	243.0	1.00	1.03	0.41	0.44	0.72	0.67
temperature (°C)	hot 467 cold –183	average 452	hot 58 cold –88	hot 20 cold –140	average –153	average –185	average –214	average –225

? QUESTIONS

4 How many planets are there in our Solar System?

5 Which planet has the largest diameter?

6 Finish this sentence to identify a trend. 'As the distance from the Sun increases, the orbit time ....'

CHALLENGE QUESTION:

7 Which planet has a day that is longer than its year?

key words: orbit planet Solar System Sun

Satellites

A satellite is any object in orbit around another.

The Moon orbits the Earth. It is the Earth's natural satellite. So far, it is the only other body in the Universe to be visited by humans. Neil Armstrong walked on the Moon's surface in July 1969.

The Earth is not the only planet to have a natural satellite. With the exception of Mercury and Venus, all of the other planets have moons.

Is the Moon a satellite?

Planet	Moons	Names of largest moons
Earth	1	Luna
Mars	2	Phobos, Deimos
Jupiter	63	Io, Europa, Ganymede, Callisto
Saturn	61	Titan, Rhea, Iapetus, Dione
Uranus	27	Cordelia, Ophelia, Bianca, Cressida
Neptune	13	Triton, Nereid, Naiad, Thalassa

Artificial satellites

There are about 3000 artificial satellites orbiting the Earth. Most of them are unmanned. These satellites are used for:

♦ communication – including television
♦ mapping – including satnav
♦ weather forecasting
♦ spying
♦ tracking.

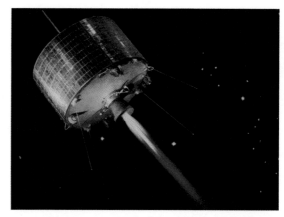

Name two uses for artificial satellites.

? QUESTIONS

8 Why is Earth a satellite?

9 Which planet has most moons?

10 Which planet has a moon called Bianca orbiting it?

CHALLENGE QUESTION:

11 Suggest why the Moon is the only other body in space visited by humans.

key words: artificial   communication   mapping   moon   satellite

The Universe

The Universe is made up of billions of galaxies.

Our galaxy is called the Milky Way.

There are about 200 billion stars in the Milky Way. The diameter of the Milky Way is so large it takes light 100 000 years to go from one side to the other. The Milky Way is a flat spiral shape – like a giant, spinning Catherine-wheel.

How many stars are there in the Milky Way?

Each of the stars in the galaxy may have a number of planets orbiting it. Stars are luminous and they provide the light for the Solar System. Anything else in the Solar System reflects light from the star. This reflected light is what enables us to see things.

Earth and the rest of the Solar System is at the edge of the Milky Way so we can see the rest of the galaxy.

Astronomical sizes

Sizes in space are very large.

But these sizes are really small compared to the size of the galaxies and the Universe.

The Milky Way is 900 000 000 000 000 000 km across.

The visible Universe has a diameter 170 000 times larger.

Scientists sometimes use scale models to help understand sizes. If the Universe was the size of the Earth, the Solar System would be smaller than a grain of sand.

Why do you think scientists use models to help understand the Universe?

	Approximate diameter in km
Moon	3500
Earth	12 700
Sun	1 400 000

? QUESTIONS

12 What is the name of the galaxy that contains the planet Mars?

13 Why can we see most of the Milky Way?

14 How long does it take light to cross the Milky Way?

CHALLENGE QUESTION:

15 Why is it impossible for us to travel through space to another galaxy?

---

key words: galaxy   Milky Way   star   Universe

PLANNING TO COLLECT DATA

Counting stars

The Universe contains billions and billions of stars. It is impossible to count them all.

We can make a reliable estimate.

The picture represents the stars seen in an area of the night sky.

YOUR TASK

Write a plan to find out how many stars there are in the area.

Answer these questions to help you write your plan.

1 What is the area of the 'sky' shown?

2 How are you going to estimate the total number of stars there?

3 What measurements will you need to make?

4 How will you convert those measurements into an estimate of the total number?

5 Write or draw out you plan as a step-by-step list.

P6 CHECKLIST

I have learnt that...

✓ space contains many stars including our Sun.

✓ the Sun is at the centre of our Solar System.

✓ the Sun is a source of light and it is very dangerous to look at it.

✓ there are eight planets in our Solar System – Mercury, Venus, Earth, Mars, Jupiter, Saturn, Uranus, Neptune.

✓ planets orbit the Sun at different speeds depending on their distance.

✓ the Moon orbits the Earth – other planets also have moons.

✓ planets and moons reflect light from the Sun which is why we can see them.

✓ our Solar System is part of the Milky Way galaxy, one of billions of galaxies in the Universe.

✓ astronomers use telescopes to study the sky but space telescopes provide more information because there is no atmosphere and no light pollution in space.

✓ manned spacecraft need resources that unmanned craft do not.

I can...

✓ interpret information about planets and other bodies in the Universe.

Alternative energy

I am a solar panel installer

These panels contain photocells. Photocells transform light into electricity. The ones on people's homes use the light from the Sun.

Many people are now having these fitted to their roofs. The electricity they produce can be used in the home. Any extra electricity is sold to the supply company.

Alternative energy sources

Most of our energy comes from fossil fuels. These are coal, oil and natural gas. The supplies of fossil fuels are running out.

The world is using more energy every year. This means we have to find alternative ways to produce electricity, power our cars and fly to our holiday destinations.

All of Earth's energy comes from the Sun, either directly or indirectly. Fossil fuels come from dead animals and plants that relied on the Sun. Fossil fuels have taken millions of years to form. They are non-renewable. We are starting to make more use of the following renewable energy sources:

♦ wind – to power wind turbines
♦ sunlight – to produce electricity and hot water
♦ water – waves, tide and hydro-electric to turn turbines and generate electricity
♦ geothermal – using the heat beneath the Earth's surface
♦ biomass – burned or fermented.

THE DAILY NEWS
www.dailynews.com   April 1 2129
Miners' last shift!

A newspaper headline from the future – the end of oil supplies could be announced in 2057 and gas in 2070.

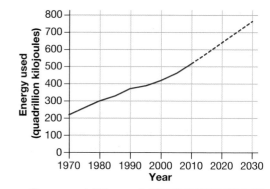

One quadrillion = 1 000 000 000 000 000 – so we use a lot of energy!

? QUESTIONS

1 What is the difference between renewable and non-renewable energy?

2 Where does all of the energy on Earth come from?

CHALLENGE QUESTION:

3 How many quadrillion kilojoules of energy is the Earth expected to use in 2030?

key words: fossil fuel   geothermal   non-renewable   renewable

Solar panels

There are two different types of solar panel fitted onto the roofs of houses.

Photovoltaic panels use photocells to produce direct current electricity. This means the current always passes through a circuit in the same direction.

As well as producing electricity for the home, these solar panels can be used in out of the way places. This means they do not need lengthy cables to connect them to the mains supply. The solar panels work best in bright sunlight, but do not work when it is dark. The electricity they produce is used to charge batteries.

Spacecraft could not operate without solar panels.

The other type of solar panel is a solar water heater. These are not very common the UK because the temperatures are not very high. In Mediterranean countries, houses may have water-filled panels on the roof and a water tank. The panels absorb the Sun's energy and transfer it into heat. The hot water is circulated and stored in a hot water tank just like in our homes.

What provides the energy to light the lamp?

How different surfaces absorb energy

A radiant heater is placed midway between two metal plates as shown. Corks are attached to the back of each plate with candle wax. After the heater is switched on, the cork on the back of the black plate drops off much sooner than the other.

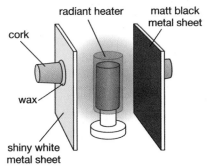

cork

radiant heater

matt black metal sheet

wax

shiny white metal sheet

Matt black surfaces absorb more energy than shiny white surfaces.

Why are these solar panel heaters not found much in the UK?

Remember, black surfaces absorb energy from the Sun – they do not attract energy. ⚠

? QUESTIONS

4 Write down **one** advantage of photocells.

5 In what conditions do photocells not work?

6 What type of surface absorbs most energy from the Sun as heat?

CHALLENGE QUESTION:

7 Suggest why solar panels containing photocells are more widely used in this country than solar panel water heaters.

key words: absorb battery energy photocell radiant

Energy from the wind

Windmills have made use of energy from the wind for 2000 years. Many were used to grind corn into flour.

Modern wind turbines look very different. Most have three blades; some have only two. Smaller turbines may have five blades. Some spin on a vertical axis producing energy from the wind blowing in any direction.

The blades of a wind turbine are similar in cross-section to an aircraft propeller. For best results, the blades need to face the wind. On some wind turbines, the housing can rotate. A rudder on the back of the turbine makes sure the blades are facing the wind. On others, the blades can change their angles to face the wind.

More energy is produced from longer blades than from shorter ones. Increasing the length of the blades also increases the height. Wind speeds increase with height.

It is now quite common to see a lot of wind turbines together. This is called a wind farm. Some wind farms are in the sea.

Advantages and disadvantages of wind turbines

The energy from the wind is renewable and free. Although wind farms occupy a large area, most of the land is available for cattle to graze or crops to be grown.

Turbines only produce electricity when the wind is blowing. If the wind speed is greater than 20 m/s, the turbines could be damaged so they need to shut down. This is done by rotating the blades so that the wind passes by without hitting the blades. People living near wind turbines complain about the noise and that the scenery has been spoiled. Birds have been killed by the blades going round.

How are modern wind turbines different to windmills?

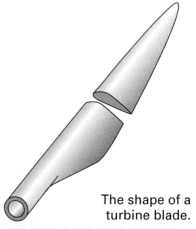
The shape of a turbine blade.

What can the land around a wind turbine be used for?

? QUESTIONS

8 What is produced from a windmill?

9 What is the advantage of a wind turbine that spins on a vertical axis?

10 Write down **two** ways that turbine blades are made to face into the wind.

CHALLENGE QUESTION:

11 Suggest why some people do not want wind farms in the Welsh mountains.

key words: blade rudder turbine wind farm

Biomass

Biomass is a source of renewable energy. It is made from many types of plant and animal waste.

Examples include:

- ◆ crop stalks
- ◆ tree thinnings
- ◆ wood pellets
- ◆ chicken and pig waste
- ◆ lawn trimmings
- ◆ gas from landfill sites.

Miscanthus plants are grown as a biomass fuel. How is the energy in this plant material released?

Although the wood and plant material is burned, the energy source is renewable because fresh crops will be planted. When biomass is burned, the heat produced is used in the same way as in a conventional power station.

Methane, which is used as a fuel, can be produced if waste products are allowed to ferment. Small-scale production can take place at homes and farms. Large-scale production takes place at sugar factories and sewage works.

Energy from tide and waves

As the tide in the ocean comes in and out, the energy from the moving water can be used to turn a turbine. The turbine turns a generator to produce electricity. Many turbines can be used together like a dam, forming a tidal barrage. Most electricity is produced where there is a large tidal range. This means there is a big height difference between low tide and high tide.

A wave generator uses the up and down motion of the waves to keep a pendulum swinging. This pendulum turns a turbine which in turn spins a generator to produce electricity.

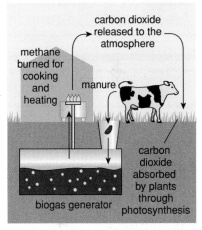

Methane is produced by fermentation of animal waste.

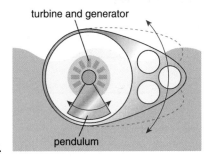

A wave generator.

? QUESTIONS

12 What is biomass?

13 Write down **two** ways in which biomass can be used to produce energy.

14 What are the advantages of using the waves and tide to produce energy?

CHALLENGE QUESTION:

15 Why are there not many places in the world where a tidal barrage could be built?

key words: biomass   methane   tidal barrage   wave

PATTERNS IN THE DATA

Wind turbine blades

The amount of electricity produced by a wind turbine depends on the length of its blades.

Wind turbines work best when the wind speed is 15 m/s.

The Danish and American Wind Energy Associations have produced data to show the maximum power output for different sizes of wind turbine.

The table shows the results.

Diameter of blades in m	Power output in kW
10	25
17	100
27	225
33	300
40	500
44	600
48	750
54	1000
64	1500
72	2000
80	2500

YOUR TASK

1 Plot a graph of the results.

2 Draw a smooth curve as a line of best fit.

3 What pattern is shown by the data?

You could use a graph plotting program for this task.

Maths Skills

Level **3** 2 1

Plot simple line graphs.

P7 CHECKLIST

I have learnt that...

✓ the Sun is a stable source of energy.

✓ fossil fuels are a limited source of energy and that demand for energy is rising.

✓ some energy sources are renewable – wind, sunlight, waves, tide, hydro-electric, geothermal and biomass.

✓ wind turbines use energy from moving wind to generate electricity.

✓ photocells produce direct current by transforming light into electricity.

✓ photocells are useful in remote areas.

✓ black matt surfaces absorb more energy than white shiny surfaces.

✓ solar panels work by circulating water heated by the Sun's radiation.

✓ biomass can be burned or fermented to produce methane.

✓ the movement of the tide and waves can turn turbines and generate electricity.

I can ...

✓ interpret data about the demand and availability of energy.

✓ evaluate the design of wind turbine blades and rudder.

Deep impacts

I am a space researcher

I work at a laboratory which looks for Near Earth Objects (NEOs). These are asteroids or comets that are on a possible collision course with Earth.

Every year, about 50 million kg of material from space hits Earth. Most of it is dust-sized particles. About 5000 kg of it is in lumps from 10 g up to 1 kg. Very rarely, larger NEOs hit Earth.

About 65 million years ago, a 10 km diameter asteroid collided with Earth. There were fires and tsunamis. There was so much dust in the air that the Sun was blocked out and Earth's temperature dropped to near freezing. Half the species on Earth, including dinosaurs, became extinct.

Meteors and meteorites

Meteors are rocks from space. As they move through space, they may collide with planets and moons. When a meteor approaches Earth, it normally burns up in the atmosphere.

Meteorites are rocks from space that successfully pass through the atmosphere and land on Earth.

Remember, meteors burn up, meteorites land on Earth. ⚠️

The Leonid meteor shower.
Explain what is happening.

❓ QUESTIONS

1 What do the letters 'NEO' stand for?

2 What is the difference between a meteor and a meteorite?

CHALLENGE QUESTION:

3 Why did dinosaurs become extinct when an asteroid struck the Earth 65 million years ago?

key words: extinct   meteor   meteorite   Near Earth Object   tsunami

Asteroids

Asteroids are rocks that were left after the Solar System was formed 4.5 billion years ago.

Most asteroids orbit the Sun between Mars and Jupiter. Like the planets, their orbit is roughly circular in shape.

Some asteroids have orbits that cross Earth's orbit. These are the ones that could collide with Earth.

The largest asteroid is called Ceres. It is nearly 1000 km in diameter. The smallest asteroids are no larger than dust particles.

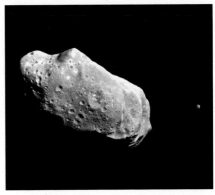

The asteroid Ida with its moon Dactyl. What is an asteroid?

Comets

Comets also orbit the Sun. Their orbits are elliptical in shape. The orbit of a typical comet passes well beyond Neptune and Pluto and inside the orbit of Mercury.

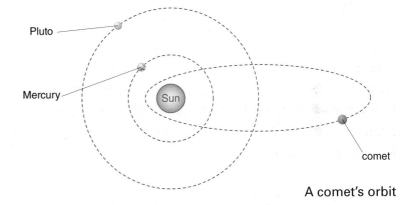

A comet's orbit

Comets are lumps of dust and ice. They vary in size from 750 m to 20 km diameter. As a comet gets nearer the Sun, the ice melts and the comet forms a tail that always points away from the Sun. The tail can be up to 150 million km long. Comet Halley is the most well-known comet. It orbits the Sun every 75 years. It was last visible from Earth in 1986.

Comet Halley in 1986. What forms the comet's tail?

? QUESTIONS

4 What shape is the orbit of a comet?

5 What is the diameter of the largest known asteroid?

6 In which direction does a comet's tail always point?

CHALLENGE QUESTION:

7 When will Comet Halley next be visible from Earth?

key words: asteroid comet elliptical tail

Impacts

When a rock from space collides with a planet or moon, it makes a crater.

The size of the crater depends on:
- ♦ the weight of the rock
- ♦ how fast the rock is travelling.

The asteroid that landed in Mexico 65 million years ago made a crater 300 km in diameter. The crater is now buried by hundreds of metres of sediment so cannot be seen.

One of the smallest craters is the Barringer Crater in Arizona, it is 1 km across.

What caused the Barringer Crater?

Giant impact

The Solar System was formed just over 4.5 billion years ago. Scientists believe that nearly 200 million years later, two planets collided. One of them was the old Earth. The other was about the same size as Mars.

The iron from both planets combined to form the core of the new Earth. The lumps of rock that were thrown out joined together to form the Moon. This started to orbit the Earth.

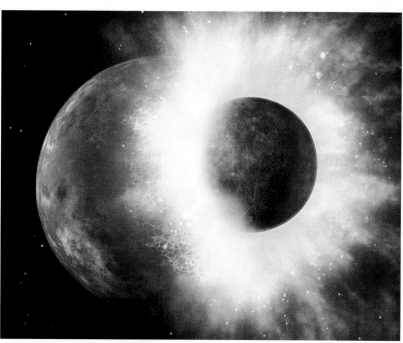

How do scientists think our Earth was formed?

? QUESTIONS

8 What is produced when an asteroid hits the Moon?

9 How many years younger is the Earth than the Solar System?

10 How was the Moon formed?

CHALLENGE QUESTION:

11 The rocks on the Moon contain the same percentage of oxygen as the rocks on Earth. Asteroids and the rocks from other planets contain different amounts of oxygen. What does this tell you about the Earth and the Moon?

key words: core   crater   orbit   weight

Searching the sky

Astronomers use large telescopes to look at the sky. The telescopes are in observatories.

Some observatories are in the middle of deserts or high up on mountains. In these places, there is not so much light pollution. Astronomers can then see a lot more.

They also make use of information sent back from space telescopes. These pictures are clearer still because there is no atmosphere in space.

Astronomers regularly discover new asteroids and comets.

They then watch them to find out their path through the Solar System. This is particularly important if they are large.

The longer astronomers keep tracking the object, the more accurately they know its path. Since they know the path of the Earth, they can work out whether the object will pass close enough to cause concern.

Any object that could pass closer than 1.3 times the distance between the Earth and Sun is a NEO. On 8 November 2011, an asteroid, called YU55, passed closer to Earth than the Moon. In terms of space distances, that was close!

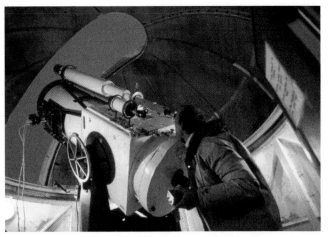
Where are the largest telescopes located?

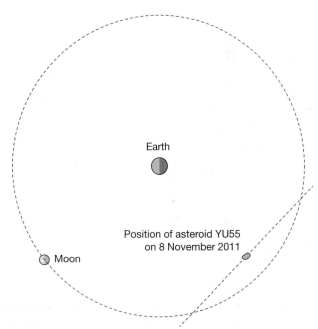

Earth

Position of asteroid YU55
on 8 November 2011

Moon

Some asteroids pass quite close to Earth.

? QUESTIONS

12 What do astronomers use to monitor asteroids and comets?

13 Why are observatories often found in deserts?

14 Why is it more important to monitor large asteroids and comets?

CHALLENGE QUESTION:

15 The distance from the Earth to the Moon is 400 000 km. How close did asteroid YU55 come to Earth?

---

key words: astronomer   observatory   telescope

REVIEWING THE METHOD
Craters

A student drops an assortment of different sized balls into a tray of sand.

The balls represent meteorites. The sand represents the surface of a planet.

She measures the diameter of the crater.

The table shows her results.

Type of ball	Height dropped in cm	Mass of ball in g	Crater diameter in mm
table tennis	50	2.5	10
golf	50	45	60
tennis	50	58	80
cricket	50	160	90
squash	50	25	70
foot	25	430	150

CAN-DO TASK

Level **3** 2 1

I can measure length/ distance accurately.

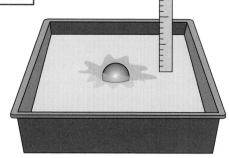

 YOUR TASK

1 Look carefully at how the student collected the data and the results of her investigation.

2 Why do you think the results are erratic?

3 How could she improve her experimental method?

4 How could she make sure her results are as precise as possible?

Maths Skills

Level 3 **2** 1

Extract and interpret information from tables.

P8 CHECKLIST

I have learnt that...

✓ the Moon was formed after another planet collided with Earth.

✓ asteroids are rocks left over when the Solar System was formed.

✓ comets are lumps of dust and ice which have elliptical orbits.

✓ the tail of a comet is formed when the ice melts as the comet approaches the Sun.

✓ meteors burn up in the Earth's atmosphere.

✓ meteorites land on the Earth's surface.

✓ asteroids have collided with the Earth in the past causing fires, tsunamis, climate change, species extinction, craters.

✓ the size of a crater depends on the speed and weight of the object causing it.

✓ astronomers monitor Near Earth Objects with large telescopes.

✓ the longer a Near Earth Object is observed, the more accurately its path can be predicted.

I can ...

✓ interpret data about possible Near Earth Object collisions.

✓ measure length/distance accurately ➡ **CAN-DO TASK Level ③**.

Driving along

I am a driving instructor

As part of the driving test, you have to know about the Highway Code and how a car works as well as being able to drive it. I always tell people that it is more important to know how to stop a car than to start it!

Stopping distances

Cars cannot stop immediately. Imagine you are driving and someone steps out in front of you. It takes time for you to react. The distance the car moves while you are reacting is the thinking distance. When your foot presses on the brake pedal, the car starts to slow down and stop. The distance the car travels while you are braking is the braking distance.

stopping distance = thinking distance + braking distance

Typical stopping distances

Thinking distance
Braking distance

20 mph 6m 6m
= 12 metres

30 mph 9m 14m
= 23 metres

50 mph 15m 38m
= 53 metres

The Highway Code shows typical thinking distances and braking distances. It assumes a dry road and a car with good brakes.

Speed limits

Speed limits were introduced to save fuel and to make roads safer. The national speed limits are 60 mph on most roads but 70 mph on motorways and other dual carriageways. In towns, the limits are usually 30 mph or 40 mph. In areas where there are special dangers, for example outside schools, the limit may be 20 mph.

If a car has an accident, the damage and injury to occupants depends on the speed of impact. If the speed doubles, the damage and injury increase by a factor of four.

Speed cameras, warning signs, road humps and chicanes are all used to reduce the speed of traffic.

ZONE
30

What is the typical stopping distance when travelling at 30 mph?

? QUESTIONS

1 Why were speed limits introduced?

2 What is the thinking distance when a car is travelling at 50 mph?

CHALLENGE QUESTION:

3 Suggest why the speed limit in a town is 30 mph.

key words: braking distance   reaction time   speed limit   thinking distance

Measuring speed

Roadside cameras can detect if a car is speeding. They take two photographs of the car as it passes over lines painted in the road. The time between the two photograph is 0.7 s and the distance between each line is about 1.6 m. When the two photographs are compared, each line passed represents a speed of 5 mph. These cameras make use of the fact that:

$$\text{speed} = \frac{\text{distance}}{\text{time}}$$

At the car showroom

There are lots of cars to choose from. As the cost of fuel rises, one important question to ask the salesman is about the car's fuel type and fuel consumption.

Today you can buy cars fuelled by petrol, diesel, LPG (liquid petroleum gas) and biofuel.

Traditional vehicles have a four-stroke engine. The diagrams shows what happens during each stroke.

Where would you put a speed camera?

CAN-DO TASK

Level   3   2   **1**

I can measure reaction time.

Petrol engine

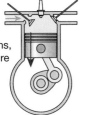

Induction
inlet valve opens, petrol air mixture taken in

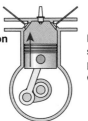

Compression
both valves closed, mixture compressed

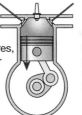

Power
spark plug fires, petrol vapour expands

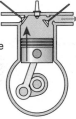

Exhaust
exhaust valve opens, waste gases forced out

Diesel engine

Induction
inlet valve opens, air taken in

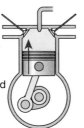

Compression
both valves closed, air compressed and gets hot

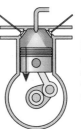

Power
fuel injected and burns, gases expand

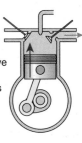

Exhaust
exhaust valve opens, waste gases forced out

❓ QUESTIONS

4 What are the **two** most common fuels used in cars?

5 What is the job of a spark plug in a petrol engine?

6 A car travels 120 km in 2 hours. What is its speed?

CHALLENGE QUESTION:

7 Why does a speed camera need to take two photographs?

key words: biofuel   diesel   petrol   speed

217

Changing gear

There are many examples of machines being used in cars. Machines allow you to use less effort to move a load.

The types of machine that work when things go round are:

♦ pulley
♦ wheel and axle
♦ gear.

Pulleys are used to change speed or direction of rotation. A pulley system consists of two or more pulley wheels linked by a belt.

In a car, a pulley system is used to link the water pump, alternator and radiator cooling fan. The belt that links them is often called the fan belt.

A wheel and axle is a machine which has a large diameter wheel and a small diameter axle. It is easier to turn the large wheel than the small axle. Inside a car, the large steering wheel is attached to a small axle.

The gears in a car allow the engine to work most efficiently and use less fuel. When you change gear, you select a pair of gears to work together.

The gear ratio is a measure of how much easier it is do the job with the gears than without.

$$\text{gear ratio} = \frac{\text{number of teeth on driven gear}}{\text{number of teeth on driver gear}}$$

How many gears does this car have?

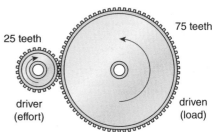

In first gear, the driver gear from the engine is smaller than the driven gear to the wheels. This means less effort is needed to start the car moving.

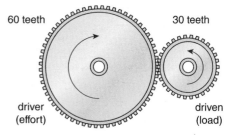

In fifth gear, the driver gear is larger than the driven gear. The driven gear rotates faster than the driving gear.

? QUESTIONS

8 What **three** machines help to make it easier to turn things?

9 Where in a car will you find a wheel and axle?

10 Which gear, driver or driven, provides the effort?

CHALLENGE QUESTION:

11 Calculate the gear ratio for the first gear of a car if there are 32 teeth on the driver gear and 80 teeth on the driven gear.

key words: gear   machine   pulley   wheel and axle

Motoring along

Some cars do not burn a fuel in their engines.

They use batteries. The batteries power an electric motor.

The batteries need to be charged. This is usually done by plugging into a mains electrical socket.

Solar powered cars use photocells to produce the electricity to charge the batteries.

The advantages of solar powered cars are:
- ♦ the energy is free
- ♦ there is no polluting waste
- ♦ fossil fuels are not depleted.

The disadvantages of solar powered cars are:
- ♦ the photocells do not produce electricity at night
- ♦ the area of photocells needs to be quite large.

The car battery supplies power to a DC electric motor, made from a coil of wire. The coil spins between the poles of a magnet. Electric current is supplied to the motor by brushes touching a contact. As the motor spins, the brushes touch opposite sides of the coil. This makes sure the motor always turns in the same direction. This arrangement is called a commutator.

The starter and the windscreen wipers of a car are both powered by motors.

> **Remember,** that motors and generators are different. A motor uses an electric current to turn. A generator is turned to produce an electric current. ⚠

What is a disadvantage of this battery powered car?

What kind of energy do solar powered car batteries use?

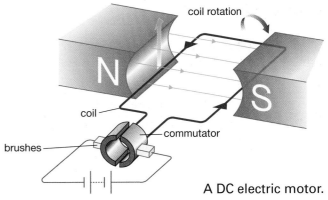

A DC electric motor.

? QUESTIONS

12 What provides the power source for an electric car?

13 Write down **one** advantage of a solar powered car.

14 How is electric current supplied to the coil of a motor?

CHALLENGE QUESTION:

15 How does a commutator make sure the current in the coil is always in the same direction?

---

key words: commutator   motor   photocell   solar powered

PROCESSING THE DATA

Model motor

The speed of rotation of a model motor is measured using a digital tachometer.

The motor is connected to a power supply and an ammeter is used to measure the current in the coil.

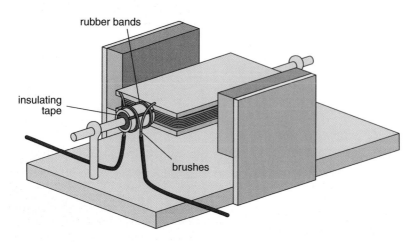

A digital tachometer records the rotation speed of the coil.

Current in A	Speed of rotation in revolutions per minute			
	1st try	2nd try	3rd try	Average
0.0	0	0	0	0
0.2	149	141	130	
0.4	257	244	249	
0.6	333	348	339	
0.8	418	412	400	
1.0	456	455	469	

Maths Skills

Level **3** 2 1

Calculate arithmetical means.

Maths Skills

Level **3** 2 1

Plot simple line graphs.

 YOUR TASK

1 Calculate the average speeds of rotation.
2 Plot a graph of speed of rotation against current.
3 Draw a smooth curve which is the line of best fit.

P9 CHECKLIST

I have learnt that...

✓ engines have four strokes – induction, compression, power and exhaust.

✓ petrol, diesel, LPG and biofuel are used as fuels in vehicles.

✓ the spark plug ignites fuel in a petrol engine but compressed gases heat and ignite fuel in a diesel engine.

✓ pulleys, gears and wheel and axles are used as machines in cars so that more load can be moved with less effort.

✓ motors have a coil, magnets, brushes and commutator.

✓ some cars have electric motors instead of engines and that cars have motors for windscreen wipers and starters.

✓ electric cars need to be charged from the mains.

✓ there are advantages and disadvantages in using solar energy to charge batteries for electric cars.

✓ speed limits vary according to the road – they help reduce fuel consumption and improve road safety.

✓ thinking distance and braking distance affect total stopping distance.

I can ...

✓ measure reaction time
⟫ **CAN-DO TASK Level** ①.

✓ interpret data on thinking, braking and stopping distances.

✓ calculate gear ratios from a knowledge of teeth numbers on the driver gear and the driven gear.

Hot stuff!

I am a bricklayer

When we build homes, the outer walls have two layers. We fill the space between them with insulation material. This is usually mineral wool, fibreglass or polystyrene blocks. All of these have air trapped in them.

Air is an insulator. Insulators do not allow heat to pass through them very easily.

If we did not put insulation in the cavity between the walls, the air would rise up into the loft when it got warm. Cold air would replace it, cooling the walls. We call this a convection current.

Heat loss from a home

Heat is lost from a home through:
- ♦ walls
- ♦ windows
- ♦ roof
- ♦ floor.
- ♦ doors

Reducing the heat lost means lower fuel bills. Less carbon dioxide will go into the atmosphere.

Double glazing has trapped air between panes of glass. Loft insulation and under floor insulation are usually mineral wool or fibreglass. They contain trapped air too.

How can insulation help people to save money?

? QUESTIONS

1 Why is it important to trap air in cavity wall insulation?

2 Write down **one** advantage of insulating a home.

CHALLENGE QUESTION:

3 Suggest why it is especially important to insulate lofts and floors.

key words: cavity wall   conductor   convection current   insulator

Energy transfer

Energy can be transferred in a number of ways.

These include:

♦ heat
♦ light
♦ sound
♦ electricity.

When energy is transferred as heat, the energy flows from a hot to a cooler body. When the fridge door is left open, energy passes from the warm kitchen into the fridge. The temperature of the kitchen drops as a result.

Temperature and heat

Temperature is a measure of how hot a body is. It is measured in degrees Celsius (°C). Heat is an energy transfer process and the energy transferred is measured in joules (J).

Heat is very useful. It can be used for:

♦ generating electricity – the energy from burning coal heats water to produce steam to turn a turbine and generator to produce electricity
♦ cooking – the energy from the burning gas, charcoal or electric element heats and cooks the food
♦ heat – energy from burning coal or wood, electric elements, water-filled radiators and hot water tanks provides our homes with the heat we need.

What will happen to the temperature inside the fridge if the door is left open?

Remember, temperature is a measure of hotness; heat is an energy transfer process. Temperature is measured in °C; energy is measured in J. ⚠

How are these people keeping warm?

How are these eggs being cooked?

? QUESTIONS

4 What units are used to measure heat flow?
5 Write down **two** uses of heat.
6 What does a thermometer measure?

CHALLENGE QUESTION:

7 Kyle leaves the front door open on a winter's day. His mum says: "Don't let the cold in." What should she have said?

key words: degree Celsius   heat   joule   temperature

Heating up and cooling down

A flask of liquid is heated using a Bunsen burner. The temperature is measured with a thermometer.

The amount of energy needed to heat the liquid depends on:

♦ the mass of liquid – more mass needs more energy
♦ the temperature change – a larger temperature change needs more energy
♦ the liquid being heated – different substances increase their temperatures at different rates.

Changing state

Sometimes the temperature does not change when a substance is heated. This happens when the substance is changing state.

There are four changes of state:

♦ melting – from solid to liquid
♦ boiling – from liquid to gas
♦ condensing – from gas to liquid
♦ freezing – from liquid to solid.

Melting and freezing happen at the melting point.

Boiling and condensing happen at the boiling point.

Sometimes a liquid changes to a gas without being heated. This happens from the surface of the liquid and is called evaporation.

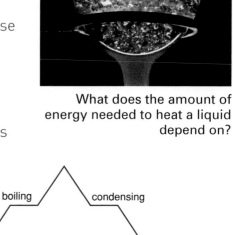

What does the amount of energy needed to heat a liquid depend on?

What will happen to these puddles on a sunny day?

How the temperature changes with time for a substance being heated and then cooled.

CAN-DO TASK

Level **3** 2 1

I can use a thermometer to measure temperature accurately.

? QUESTIONS

8 What is a change of state?

9 It takes 3 minutes to boil 100 g of water in a beaker. How long does it take to boil 200 g of water using the same beaker and heater? Choose from 2 minutes / 3 minutes / 4 minutes / 6 minutes.

10 How does a substance change when it evaporates?

CHALLENGE QUESTION:

11 Copy the heating and cooling graph. Add labels to show when the substance is a solid, a liquid and a gas.

key words: boil   condense   evaporate   freeze   melt

Energy from the Sun

The largest solar furnace is in France. A bank of mirrors track the Sun and reflect light onto a large parabolic reflector. This focuses light onto a container the size of a large cooking pot.

The energy is absorbed by the container and its contents. They get hotter. The temperature can reach 3000 °C or more.

At these temperatures, brick melts and a copper coin boils in 25 seconds!

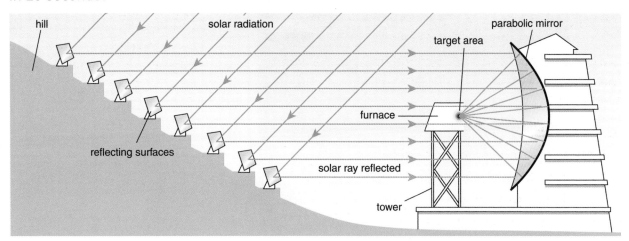

How a solar furnace works.

Some solar furnaces can be used to generate electricity. The container at the focus of the reflector contains water. When heated this produces steam to drive a turbine. The turbine turns a generator, which produces electricity.

On a smaller scale, a curved reflector can be used to focus energy from the Sun onto a cooking pot where food can be cooked or water boiled.

Solar furnaces and cookers produce free energy with no pollution.

What does the reflector in this solar cooker do?

? QUESTIONS

12 What shape is the reflector of a solar furnace?

13 Write down **one** use of a solar furnace.

14 What is the advantage of cooking on a solar cooker?

CHALLENGE QUESTION:

15 The hill opposite the solar furnace in France has many plane (flat) mirrors. They track the Sun and reflect light onto the curved reflector. Why is it better to have these mirrors than the Sun shining directly onto the curved reflector?

key words: focus   furnace   parabolic   reflector

225

PLANNING TO COLLECT DATA

Effective lagging

Lagging hot water pipes and hot water tanks reduces heat loss.

The amount of heat loss depends on the thickness of lagging.

YOUR TASK

Write a plan to find out how the thickness of lagging affects the rate of cooling of water in a beaker.

1 How many different thicknesses of lagging will you need to identify a pattern?

2 Does it matter what the starting temperature of the water is?

3 How long will you allow the water to cool for?

4 How often will you record temperature?

5 What graphs will you draw?

6 Write or draw out your final plan as a step-by-step list.

P10 CHECKLIST

I have learnt that...

✓ energy can be transferred as heat.

✓ heat is used for cooking, generating electricity and heating.

✓ energy flows from a hot to a cold body.

✓ heat is measured in joules and temperature in degrees Celsius.

✓ the energy needed to heat an object depends on its mass, temperature change and the material it is made from.

✓ light from the Sun can be focused by a curved mirror and the energy used for heating.

✓ solar furnaces use the focused light energy from the Sun.

✓ hot air rises and is replaced by colder air.

✓ insulators do not allow the flow of heat and conductors, for example metals, do allow the flow of heat.

✓ insulating the home reduces heat loss.

I can ...

✓ use a thermometer to measure temperature accurately
➡ **CAN-DO TASK Level** ③.

✓ interpret data on heating and cooling.

✓ interpret data on home insulation.

✓ design and do an experiment to find out the best takeaway food packaging.

Nuclear power

I am a technician at a nuclear power station

I have to be careful that I am not exposed to too much nuclear radiation. I always wear a film badge. This allows the Health and Safety Officers to check how much radioactivity I have been exposed to.

When I handle radioactive material, I use tongs and handle it for the shortest time possible.

Sometimes I have to wear protective clothing. Often I work behind lead or leaded glass screens. This shielding reduces the amount of radiation I am exposed to.

I always make sure that any radioactive material is clearly labelled.

Nuclear safety

The Health Protection Agency has overall responsibility for monitoring and advising on nuclear safety.

Because there could be dangerous situations when handling radioactive material, it is important that an independent body does the monitoring.

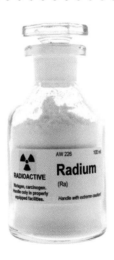

Remember, a person does not become radioactive if they are exposed to radioactivity.

Why must radioactive materials always be labelled?

? QUESTIONS

1 Why must workers at a nuclear power station wear film badges?

2 Write down **three** precautions to take when using radioactive material.

CHALLENGE QUESTION:

3 Give **one** example which shows the importance of having an independent body to monitor nuclear safety.

---

key words: film badge   nuclear   radiation   shielding

Power stations

Power stations use generators to make electricity. In a simple generator the ends of a length of wire are connected to a voltmeter. When the wire is held between the poles of a magnet, nothing happens. When the wire is moved upwards between the poles, the voltmeter needle moves. When the wire is moved downwards, the needle moves in the opposite direction. A changing magnetic field produces a current in the wire.

A simple generator.

In a power station generator a magnet spins inside a coil of wire. This means the magnetic field through the coil is changing. A current is produced in the coil.

A generator at a power station.

The generator at a power station has an electromagnet rotating inside coils of wire. The magnetic field is produced by the rotor coils. The electric current is produced in the stator coils.

Remember, no electricity is supplied to a generator – it produces electricity. ⚠

Model generator

A model generator can be used to investigate what happens when:

♦ the coil is spun at different speeds
♦ the strength of the magnetic field changes
♦ the number of turns on the coil changes.

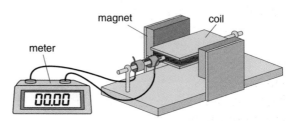

In a model generator, the coil spins and the magnet is stationary.

The results from the model show that, for a generator in a power station, the voltage increases when:

♦ the magnet spins faster
♦ the magnetic field is stronger
♦ there are more turns on the coil.

❓ QUESTIONS

4 What spins in a power station generator?

5 What happens to the voltage produced if the coil of a model generator spins slower?

6 Which coils produce the magnetic field in a power station generator?

CHALLENGE QUESTION:

7 Jenna uses a dynamo on her bike for the lights. Why do the lights go out when she stops at a junction?

---

key words: coil   dynamo   electromagnet   generator

Nuclear power station

The nuclear reactor produces heat which boils the water. The steam produced turns the turbine. The turbine drives the generator, making electricity.

At a conventional power station, the water is heated by coal, oil or gas. At a nuclear power station, the energy to heat the water comes from uranium.

Uranium is a non-renewable radioactive metal. When it is processed it can be very unstable. When atoms of uranium are unstable, they split and release a lot of energy. A freely moving particle, called a neutron, hits the uranium and causes it to split. More neutrons are released. They go on to hit more atoms and so on. This is called a chain reaction.

Hinkley Point nuclear power station in Somerset. Suggest why it is positioned near the sea.

Advantages and disadvantages of nuclear power

Nuclear energy provides cleaner electricity than conventional power stations. Nothing is burned so no carbon dioxide is released. Carbon dioxide contributes to global warming. There are no smoke particles. There is no sulfur dioxide. (This forms acid rain.) Most nuclear power stations are near the coast. This means sea water is used for cooling and there is no need for cooling towers. This reduces the amount of water vapour produced.

A lot of radioactivity can escape if there is a serious accident at a nuclear power station. One of the products from a nuclear power station is plutonium. Plutonium is also used to make nuclear bombs.

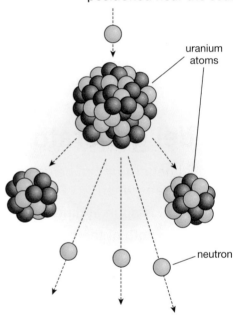

uranium atoms

neutron

The chain reaction that happens when uranium breaks down is called nuclear fission.

? QUESTIONS

8 What is the energy source at a nuclear power station?

9 How is a turbine made to turn a generator?

10 Write down **one** advantage and **one** disadvantage of using nuclear power.

CHALLENGE QUESTION:

11 The UK government is proposing to build more nuclear reactors. Give reasons why you support or disagree with the proposal.

key words: chain reaction   neutron   turbine   uranium

Nuclear waste

A nuclear power station produces waste. The waste is radioactive and harmful. It can remain radioactive for thousands of years. It has to be disposed of carefully.

Some waste, that is not very radioactive, can be sent to special land fill sites.

Waste that is more radioactive is stored deep underground. It is often mixed with molten glass. The result is safer to handle.

Some waste is reprocessed and can be reused in a nuclear power station.

Very radioactive waste is stored 700 m underground. Suggest why.

Many people are worried about radioactive waste being transported around the country. It usually goes by rail in special flasks. The train operating company tried to stop people worrying. They arranged for a train to crash into a stationary flask at a speed of 100 mph. The flask was filled with steel rods. These were the same size as the waste that is transported.

What was the aim of this flask and train experiment?

The flask was slightly scratched but its contents were safe. The locomotive was wrecked.

? QUESTIONS

12 Where can low level radioactive waste be disposed of?

13 What is mixed with high level waste to make it safer?

14 How is most radioactive waste transported?

CHALLENGE QUESTION:

15 The train crash flask had steel rods to represent the waste. Why were they in the flask?

key words: power station   radioactive   reprocess   waste

231

PROCESSING THE DATA
Bicycle dynamo

A bicycle dynamo generates electricity when it is turned.

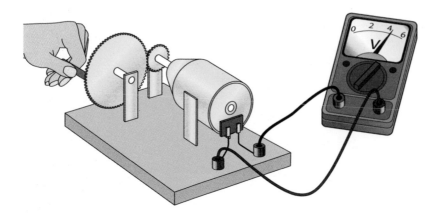

The dynamo is turned at a steady rate. The reading on the voltmeter is recorded. The experiment is repeated, each time the speed of turning the dynamo is changed.

The table shows the results.

Turns per minute	Voltage in volts			
	1st try	2nd try	3rd try	average
20	1.2	1.5	0.9	
40	2.6	2.3	2.3	
60	3.4	3.9	3.5	
80	4.7	4.9	4.8	
100	6.1	6.1	5.8	

 YOUR TASK

1 Calculate the average voltage.
2 Plot a line graph of voltage against turns per minute.
3 Draw a straight line which is the line of best fit.

CAN-DO TASK
Level **3** 2 1

I can plot a line graph.

Maths Skills
Level 3 **2** 1

Recognise and use numbers to one decimal place.

Maths Skills
Level **3** 2 1

Calculate arithmetical means.

P11 CHECKLIST

I have learnt that...

✓ electricity is made when the magnetic field through a coil of wire changes.

✓ the amount of electricity is increased if the magnetic field, turns on the coil or speed of movement increases.

✓ generators in power stations use electromagnets.

✓ radioactive materials can be handled safely if correct precautions are taken.

✓ exposure to radioactivity can be monitored with a film badge.

✓ uranium is a non-renewable metal used as the source of energy in a nuclear power station.

✓ energy is released when uranium atoms are split.

✓ nuclear power stations produce harmful radioactive waste that must be disposed of carefully.

✓ plutonium is a waste product from nuclear power stations and can be used to make nuclear bombs.

✓ nuclear safety is controlled and monitored by an independent national organisation.

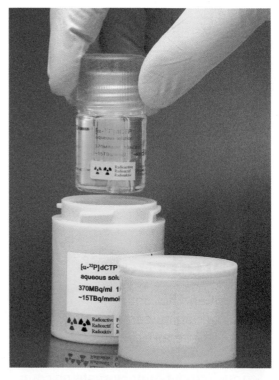

I can ...

✓ label a diagram of a generator.

✓ plot a line graph
➠**CAN-DO TASK Level** ③.

Full spectrum

I am a fire-fighter

My job can be very dangerous. When we arrive at a fire, we need to know if anyone is trapped inside. Thermal imaging cameras allow us to see through smoke.

The heat given off by the human body means we know where the person is. We also use thermal imaging cameras to find areas where a fire may be that we cannot see.

Infrared radiation

All warm and hot bodies give off infrared radiation. Thermal imaging cameras detect this radiation. Thermal imaging cameras are used by many people including:

How can fire-fighters 'see' through smoke?

♦ search and rescue teams – for finding people who are lost in mountains, forests or countryside
♦ police in helicopters – for night-time chases
♦ photographers – for night-time photography of wild animals
♦ surveyors – to look at heat loss from buildings.

Passive infrared sensors (PIRs) are used for burglar alarms. They detect the body heat of the intruder.

Some computers and mobile phones transmit and receive data over short distances using infrared signals. Remote controllers for televisions and other household devices also use infrared radiation.

Any form of heater for example fire, toaster or cooker, emits infrared radiation.

> **Remember,** infrared radiation does not cause sunburn. ⚠️

? QUESTIONS

1 What does a thermal imaging camera detect?

2 Where is a PIR used?

CHALLENGE QUESTION:

3 How can an observer in a police helicopter identify a car in a car park that has been recently parked?

key words: heat   infrared   radiation   thermal imaging

Electromagnetic spectrum

Infrared radiation is part of a group of waves called the electromagnetic spectrum. Other members of the group include:

♦ ultraviolet
♦ microwave
♦ radio
♦ visible light.

All of these waves travel at the speed of light, 300 000 km/s.

Visible light

White light can be split into the seven colours of the rainbow:

♦ red
♦ orange
♦ yellow
♦ green
♦ blue
♦ indigo
♦ violet.

To help remember the order, you can use a mnemonic like **Richard of York gave battle in vain**.

These colours form the visible spectrum.

You can see the spectrum when white light is split by passing through a glass prism or through raindrops or is reflected from a CD.

> **Remember,** radio waves travel at the speed of light, not the speed of sound. ⚠️

What has the white light passed through to create a rainbow?

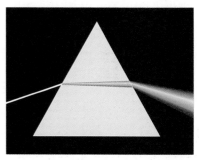

Can you count all seven colours of the spectrum and list them in the order they appear?

? QUESTIONS

4 What is the speed of microwaves?

5 Which colour is between orange and green in the visible spectrum?

6 Write down **three** types of radiation from the electromagnetic spectrum.

CHALLENGE QUESTION:

7 Light changes direction and splits up when it enters a prism. Which colour changes direction the least?

key words: electromagnetic spectrum   light   prism   spectrum

Lasers

'Laser' stands for 'Light Amplification by Stimulated Emission of Radiation'. A laser produces a very intense beam of light which is very narrow. If a laser is shone onto a target 1 km away, the spread of the beam is less than 1 m.

The energy from a laser is capable of cutting through sheets of metal very accurately.

Lasers are also used for:

♦ reading CDs
♦ light shows
♦ pointers
♦ weapons guidance
♦ bar-code readers.

You should never point a laser pointer into anyone's eyes. They can cause temporary or permanent blindness.

How is this metal sheet being cut?

Radio waves

Radio waves allow us to communicate and transmit data around the world at the speed of light.

A radio receiver has a metal aerial. The radio waves create an electrical signal in the aerial. This signal goes into an electric circuit. It is amplified and becomes the sound we hear.

Laptops also use wireless technology to transmit and receive information from the Internet and other devices.

Where are the radio waves turned into an electrical signal?

? QUESTIONS

8 How can a laser pointer be dangerous?

9 How is a laser used in a supermarket?

10 What is the job of an aerial?

CHALLENGE QUESTION:

11 How has wireless technology changed the way we communicate with each other?

key words: aerial   laser   radio   wireless

Microwaves

Most foods can be microwaved. The food cooks because the energy from certain microwaves makes the water or fat particles in the food vibrate. When they vibrate they get hotter. The heat is then conducted through the food until it is all cooked.

Other microwaves are used for radar. Weather forecasters look at radar images to help them predict the weather. The radar detects clouds and rainfall. Forecasters look at how the clouds and rain move. They then predict what will happen in the future.

How do microwaves cook food?

All of the information sent to and from satellites uses microwaves. They have a greater range than radio waves and can pass through the Earth's atmosphere.

Mobile phones also use microwaves for transmitting the signal. Whilst they provide a very convenient way of keeping in touch, there is some evidence that a lot of exposure to microwaves can be harmful.

A lot of scientists are investigating the possible harm caused by microwaves. Their results do not always agree.

Is texting a safer way to use a mobile phone?

> **THE DAILY NEWS**
> www.dailynews.com   March 16 2012
> ## Mobile phones more dangerous than smoking

> *The Sunday Blah*
> ## Mobiles don't raise cancer risk

> ## Mobiles cut sperm count, says report

> **Warning:** Using a mobile phone while pregnant can seriously damage your baby

CAN-DO TASK

Level   3   2   **1**

I can produce a poster on the safe use of mobile phones.

The latest, reliable research has stated that there is some evidence linking mobile phones to cancer, but it is too weak to make any strong conclusions.

❓ QUESTIONS

12 What type of radiation is used by mobile phones?

13 What is shown on a weather radar picture?

14 Why are radio waves not suitable for satellite communication?

CHALLENGE QUESTION:

15 What advice could be given to people using mobile phones to reduce the health risks?

key words: cancer   microwave   mobile phone   radar

PLANNING TO COLLECT DATA

Visible spectrum

A spectrum is produced when a narrow ray of white light is shone through a 60° prism.

The spectrum can be displayed on a screen.

The width of the spectrum changes as the angle of incidence at the first surface of the prism changes.

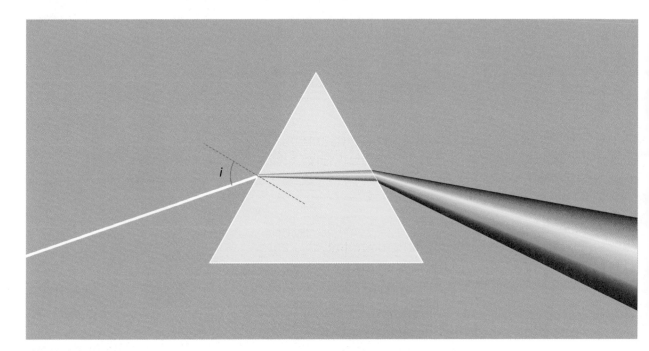

YOUR TASK

Write a plan to find out how the width of the spectrum on a screen changes with the angle of incidence, *i*.

1 How many different angles of incidence will you need?

2 What needs to be kept the same to make it a fair test?

3 What measurements will you need to make?

4 Will you need to repeat readings and if so how many times?

5 How will you present your results?

6 Write or draw out you plan as a step-by-step list.

P12 CHECKLIST

I have learnt that...

✓ visible light is one of a group of waves that form the electromagnetic spectrum.

✓ all waves in the electromagnetic spectrum travel at the speed of light.

✓ rainbows are a natural example of the visible spectrum which can also be formed by a glass prism.

✓ lasers produce intense narrow beams of light that have many uses.

✓ warm and hot bodies emit infrared radiation.

✓ infrared radiation is used for thermal imaging, night photography, burglar alarms, remote controllers, heating and short-range data transmission.

✓ microwaves are used for cooking, satellite communication, radar and mobile phones.

✓ there may be some health risks in using mobile phones.

✓ radio waves produce electrical signals in aerials.

✓ radio waves are used for world-wide communication and wireless links between computer devices.

I can ...

✓ produce a poster on the safe use of mobile phones
➠**CAN-DO TASK Level** ①.

✓ list the colours of the visible spectrum in order.

✓ interpret information into the effects of mobile phone usage.

Medical rays

I work for a leading cancer charity

Our aim is to beat cancer through research and education. Thanks to the work we are doing, more people are surviving cancer than ever before.

My job involves going into schools and talking to young people about skin cancer in particular.

Suntan or skin cancer

Many people think that a suntan is healthy. Ultraviolet radiation is responsible for causing a suntan. It affects a pigment in the skin called melanin and causes it to darken. Some people spend too much time in the sun or on a sun bed. If this happens they can get sunburn or even skin cancer. Skin cancer is now one of the most common cancers in the UK. Even young people are dying as a result of spending too much time in the sun.

THE DAILY NEWS

www.dailynews.com   June 1 2012

Skin cancer can be a teenage killer

Supa **SOL** cream SPF **30**

To work out how long you can stay in the sun, multiply the normal burn time by the SPF number.

Safe in the sun

To stay safe in the sun you should:

♦ cover up – wear loose fitting clothing, sunglasses and a wide-brimmed hat

♦ apply a high sun protection factor (SPF) sunscreen – the higher the factor, the longer you can stay in the sun safely

♦ reduce the time you spend in the sun

♦ be aware that any change in shape or colour of existing moles may be a sign of skin cancer and a visit to the doctor is essential.

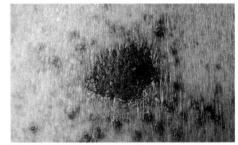

Why is skin cancer so common?

? QUESTIONS

1 Write down **one** danger from using a sunbed too often.

2 Write down **three** ways of staying safe in the sun.

CHALLENGE QUESTION:

3 Jane is sunbathing. Without sunscreen she can stay in the sun for 15 minutes. How long can she stay in the sun if she uses sunscreen with SPF 20?

---

key words: melanoma   skin cancer   sunscreen   ultraviolet

Medical uses of ultraviolet radiation

Ultraviolet radiation is used to treat skin conditions like psoriasis and atopic dermatitis. Psoriasis is raised patches of dead skin that have not been shed. Atopic dermatitis is a form of eczema.

Ultraviolet radiation kills microbes so it is also used for sterilising rooms and equipment. It is also used to clean blood for transfusions.

What is this UV lamp being used for?

Background radiations

Ultraviolet radiation, X-rays and gamma rays are members of a group of waves that form the electromagnetic spectrum. They all occur naturally and are around us the whole time. This radiation is called background radiation.

Radiation can damage living cells. The effect depends on the type and how much radiation the cells are exposed to.

The amount of radiation is measured in units called sieverts. The table shows some of the effects.

The amount of background radiation is about 0.002 sieverts.

Amount of radiation in sieverts	Effect on human body
0.0–0.2	no symptoms, possible increase in risk of cancer
0.2–0.5	decrease in red blood cell count
0.5–1.0	mildly sick
1.0–2.0	tired, sick all day
2.0–3.0	hair loss, sick for several days
3.0–6.0	60% risk of dying within a month
over 6.0	will die within a month

? QUESTIONS

4 How can psoriasis be treated?

5 What is background radiation?

6 Write down **three** types of radiation in the electromagnetic spectrum.

CHALLENGE QUESTION:

7 Karl has been exposed to 0.8 sieverts of radiation. How will this affect him?

key words: electromagnetic spectrum   microbes   radiation

Diagnosis and treatment

Before a doctor can treat an illness, she has to diagnose what is wrong. This will involve asking a patient about their symptoms. She may also want to see inside the body.

One way of seeing inside the body is by surgery. This involves cutting open the body and looking inside. All types of surgery have risks. The risks are higher if the patient has been anaesthetised.

Why does a doctor ask a patient for their symptoms?

X-rays

It is usually possible to see inside the body without surgery. X-rays pass through soft tissue but are absorbed by bone. This means that a shadow picture is produced on an X-ray film. When the film is processed, the bone appears white.

X-rays are a very good way of finding out about possible broken bones. After the bone has been repaired, another X-ray will show that the repair has been successful.

There is a risk of using X-rays. They can damage living cells. The risk from X-rays is less than the risk from surgery or from not taking any action. On balance, it is better to take an X-ray.

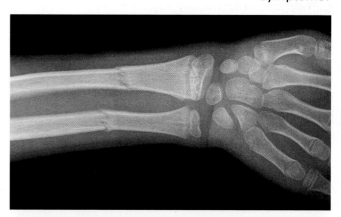

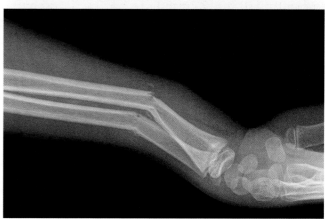

What does this X-ray show?

❓ QUESTIONS

8 What is the benefit to a patient of being X-rayed?

9 What colour represents bone on an X-ray film?

10 Why is an X-ray not suitable to find out about damage to soft tissue?

CHALLENGE QUESTION:

11 Describe the difference between diagnosis and treatment.

key words: diagnosis   surgery   treatment   X-ray

Gamma radiation

Gamma rays have very similar properties to X-rays. They are both very penetrating. They can pass through walls of lead or concrete. Gamma rays are more penetrating than X-rays.

Radiographers who use X-rays or gamma rays stand behind thick walls to reduce the amount of radiation they receive. Patients are sometimes covered with a lead apron before being X-rayed.

Gamma radiation is often used as a tracer. A radioactive liquid is injected into the bloodstream. Its passage through the body is checked with a gamma camera linked to a computer.

Active cancers take up blood more readily than healthy tissue. The image shows a breast cancer (coloured red). This is a common form of cancer in women. It can be treated by first removing the cancer by surgery. Afterwards, the patient is treated with radiotherapy and chemotherapy. Radiotherapy involves high doses of gamma radiation. Chemotherapy involves treating with drugs.

Gamma rays, just like X-rays, are harmful and the risk of using them has to be weighed against the benefits.

> **Remember,** radiotherapy and chemotherapy are different ways of treating cancer. ⚠

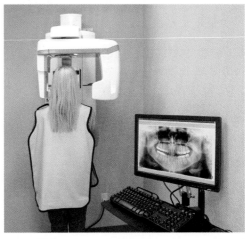

Why does this patient wear a lead apron during an X-ray of her teeth?

> **Remember,** gamma radiation is not used to take X-rays. ⚠

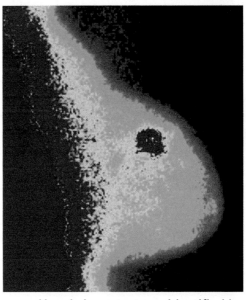

How is breast cancer identified by gamma radiation?

❓ QUESTIONS

12 What is a tracer?

13 How do radiographers reduce the amount of radiation they receive?

14 State **one** difference between gamma rays and X-rays.

CHALLENGE QUESTION:

15 Describe the difference between radiotherapy and chemotherapy.

---

key words: chemotherapy gamma rays radiotherapy tracer

PATTERNS IN THE DATA
Lead shielding

Lead sheets are placed between a source of gamma rays and a detector.

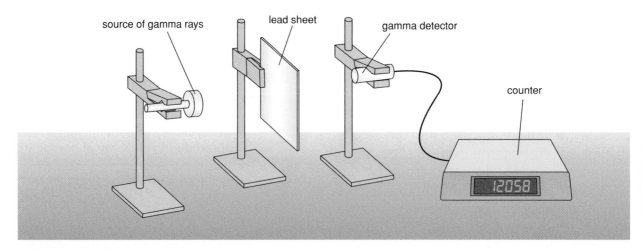

The number of gamma rays detected in one minute is counted. Different thicknesses of lead sheet are used.

The table shows the results.

Thickness of lead in mm	Counts per minute			
	1st try	2nd try	3rd try	average
2	625	660	635	640
4	145	180	155	160
6	66	60	84	70
8	55	30	35	40
10	24	23	31	26

🔍 YOUR TASK

1 Plot a graph of the results.

2 Draw a smooth curve as a line of best fit.

3 What pattern is shown by the data?

You could use a graph plotting program for this task.

Maths Skills

Level **3** 2 1

Plot simple line graphs.

P13 CHECKLIST

I have learnt that...

✓ diagnosis involves finding out what is wrong and treatment is about putting it right.

✓ surgery has risks.

✓ ultraviolet radiation has medical uses.

✓ exposure to ultraviolet radiation can cause suntan, sunburn and skin cancer.

✓ covering up, using sunscreen, reducing the time in the sun can reduce the risk of harm from ultraviolet radiation.

✓ X-rays are absorbed by bone but pass through soft tissue.

✓ gamma radiation is very penetrating.

✓ gamma cameras can be used to trace the path of a radioactive liquid around the body.

✓ X-rays and gamma rays can kill living cells but their use can be beneficial and any risk balanced against the harm.

✓ background radiations from the electromagnetic spectrum are all around us.

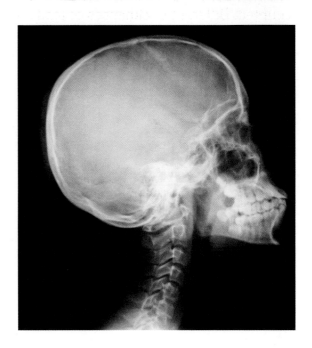

I can ...

✓ interpret data on the use of sunscreen.

✓ interpret data on radiation doses and harmful effects.

⫸ CAN-DO checklist

Use this checklist to see what you can do now and to track your progress. Go back to the topics if you need reminding or to practice. Level 1 task checklist is for a Bronze award, Level 2 is for a Silver award and Level 3 is for a Gold award.

Level 1		
Task		**Item**
1	I can measure a person's breathing rate or pulse.	**B1** Dead or alive
		B7 Gasping for breath
2	Given information I can match an animal to where it lives or when it lived.	**B3** Extinction
		B8 Creepy crawlies
3	I can measure the effect of caffeine on heart rate.	**B9** Fooling your senses
		B11 Drugs in society
4	I can safely carry out a food test for starch.	**B5** Healthy eating
5	I can use a measuring cylinder to measure volume.	**C1** Acids and alkalis
		C8 Restless Earth
6	I can identify some common metals: iron (using a magnet) copper, aluminium and lead (by sight and touch).	**C4** Heavy metal?
7	I can add results to a bar chart.	**B12** My genes
		C8 Restless Earth
8	I can measure reaction time.	**C9** How fast? How slow?
		P9 Driving along
9	I can separate a simple mixture (e.g. iron filings/ aluminium, salt/sand).	**C10** Sorting out
10	I can take a set of fingerprints.	**C11** CSI plus
11	I can write a message in mirror writing.	**P5** Let there be light!
12	I can produce a poster on the safe use of mobile phones.	**P12** Full spectrum

Level 2		
Task		**Item**
13	I can read data from a graph.	**B2** Babies
		B12 My genes
14	I can collect (scientific) information about an endangered or extinct species.	**B3** Extinction
15	I can safely carry out a food test for glucose.	**B5** Healthy eating
16	I can make a leaflet to warn old people of the dangers of hypothermia.	**B6** Control systems
17	I can carry out a test to show the presence of carbon dioxide.	**B7** Gasping for breath
		C1 Acids and alkalis
		C6 Clean air
18	I can use universal indicator solution to find pH.	**B10** Food factory
		C1 Acids and alkalis
19	I can make a paint sample and prove that it works.	**C3** Colours and smells
20	I can make measurements to test a property of a fibre or fabric.	**C5** Fibres and fabrics
21	I can make a chromatogram.	**C10** Sorting out
		C11 CSI plus
22	I can make a poster to warn about the dangers of carbon monoxide poisoning.	**C12** Fuels
23	I can read a domestic electricity meter.	**P2** Our electricity supply
24	I can use a newton meter to measure force.	**P4** Pushes and pulls

Level 3		
Task		**Item**
25	I can record my daily protein intake.	**B5** Healthy eating
26	I can use a thermometer to measure temperature accurately.	**B6** Control systems
		C3 Colours and smells
		P10 Hot stuff!
27	I can carry out a simple survey of a habitat.	**B8** Creepy crawlies
28	I can measure length/distance accurately.	**P8** Deep impacts
29	I can extract a sample of copper from its ore.	**C4** Heavy metal?
30	I can make and then test a sample of mortar for its strength.	**C7** Strong stuff
31	I can find the location of ten earthquakes or volcanoes and put them on a map.	**C8** Restless Earth
32	I can measure time accurately (e.g. to time a chemical reaction).	**C9** How fast? How slow?
		P4 Pushes and pulls
33	I can do a test to compare the quantity of vitamin C in fruit juices.	**C13** What's added to our food?
34	I can use a plotting compass to map a magnetic field.	**P3** Attractive forces
35	I can measure the speed of a moving object.	**P4** Pushes and pulls
36	I can plot a line graph.	**P11** Nuclear power

▥▶ Glossary

A

acid rain   water in clouds with a pH less than 7

adaptation   features of an organism that help it survive

additive   chemical added to food

adhesive   sticks to something

aerial   metal rod which receives radio signals and changes them into electrical signals

alloy   mixture of a metal and another element

amplitude   the maximum amount a particle in a wave moves from its rest position

analogue (signal)   a signal which can have any value

antibiotic   drug taken to treat illness caused by bacteria

antibodies   chemicals made by white blood cells which attack microbes

antioxidant   chemical that stops the effect of oxygen

artery   blood vessel that takes blood away from the heart

artificial sweetener   chemicals used instead of sugar to sweeten food and drink

asteroid   a lump of rock orbiting the Sun, too small to be called a planet

asthma   an illness that stops people breathing properly

atmosphere   mixture of gases we call air that surrounds Earth

B

bacteria   microscopic single cells that can cause disease

binder   sticks paint to a surface

biofuel   a fuel that is made from living things or their waste

biomass   dead plant or animal material that can be used as fuel

boiling point   temperature when all of a liquid turns to a gas

braking distance   the distance it takes to stop a moving vehicle

C

caffeine   chemical that increases heart rate – found in coffee

capillary   very small blood vessel

carbohydrate   type of food that is eaten for energy

carbon   a black solid (soot), a non-metal

carbon dioxide   a colourless gas that turns limewater milky

carbon monoxide   colourless, odourless, poisonous gas made when fuels burn in limited oxygen

carnivore   animal that eats other animals

catalyst   speeds up a reaction without being used up

catalytic convertor   a device fitted to exhausts to remove pollutants

cavity wall   the outer wall of a building formed from two walls with an air gap between them

cells   smallest unit of living things

cement   a substance used to make mortar and concrete

centrifuge   method of separating solids from liquids by very fast spinning

chemotherapy   treatment of cancer using chemicals

chicane   a section of road with sharp bends which forces drivers to slow down

chromatography   separating coloured dyes

chromosome   structure in the nucleus of a cell that contains genes

clone   genetically identical living things

comet   a lump of dust and ice in an elliptical orbit around the Sun

compass   a pivoted magnet that swings to point towards magnetic North

composite   two or more materials used together

concrete   cement mixed with sand, stones and water

condense   to change from a gas to a liquid

conduct   allows heat and electricity to pass through easily

continental drift plates moving slowly on the Earth's surface

convection current transfer of heat through a liquid or gas – the hotter liquid or gas rises, the cooler liquid or gas falls to take its place

converging the narrowing of a beam of light towards a focus

convex (lens) lens that is thicker in the middle than at the edges

corrode reacts with oxygen

cosmic ray radiation from space

crater hole caused by the impact from an asteroid or meteorite

crude oil dark, sticky, toxic liquid

crumple zone part of a car designed to fold and absorb energy in a collision

cytoplasm part of the cell where most chemical reactions take place

D

decanting pouring off a liquid, leaving a solid behind

demagnetise to stop being a magnet

density mass divided by volume – how heavy something is for its size

detergent molecule with a 'head' and a 'tail' used for cleaning

diabetes condition which means you cannot control your blood sugar level

diagnosis deciding what a particular illness or problem is after examination

dialysis removing salts from the blood outside the body

diesel fuel for cars, lorries, trains and buses

digital (signal) a signal which can have only two values

dissolve when a solid mixes with a liquid so it cannot be seen

distillation separates a pure liquid from a mixture

DNA chemical carrying the genetic code

drag a force which slows down something moving through a liquid or a gas

drug chemical that affects the mind or body

ductile can be pulled and shaped

dynamo device that converts movement energy into electricity

E

E numbers approved food additives

effector part of the body that responds to a stimulus e.g. muscle

elastic ability of a material to stretch and then return to its original length

electric meter meter used by the electricity supply company to record how much electricity has been used

electrode the point at which an electric current enters or leaves a battery

electrolyte solution that conducts electricity

electromagnet device made from iron which is magnetised only when a current passes through a coil around the iron

electromagnetic spectrum group of transverse waves with different frequencies but which all travel at the speed of light

electroplating using electricity to cover a metal in another metal

elliptical oval shaped

endangered animal or plant close to extinction

environment the surroundings

enzyme chemical that speeds up reactions

Epipen device used to inject someone who has a severe allergic reaction

evaporate change from a liquid into a gas by heating or leaving to dry

evolution the gradual change in living organisms over millions of years

excretion getting rid of waste from the body

extinct no longer in existence

F

fabrics different types of materials used to make clothes

fermentation when yeast changes sugar into alcohol and carbon dioxide

fertilisation when a sperm joins with an egg

fertiliser chemical used to help plants grow

fibres thin strands of material used to make a fabric

film badge a badge which monitors the amount of radiation a worker has been exposed to

filter used to separate a solid from a solution

finite   a certain amount left

foetus   baby before it is born

food chain   simple diagram that shows the feeding relationships between animals and plants

food web   diagram showing how food chains link together

fossil fuel   coal, oil or natural gas made from decayed living things millions of years ago

fractional distillation   separating liquids with different boiling points

freeze   to change from a liquid to a solid

frequency   the number of vibrations per second, measured in hertz

friction   a force that acts between two surfaces in contact with each other

fuels   chemicals that burn to make heat

fungus   microbes that can cause diseases like athlete's foot

furnace   container heated to very high temperatures

G

galaxy   large, self-contained collection of stars and planets

gamma rays   radiation produced by radioactive materials

gear   toothed wheel which turns or is turned by another toothed wheel

gene   part of a chromosome that codes for a characteristic

generator   device that converts movement energy into electricity

genetic disease   disease caused by faulty genes

geothermal   heat beneath the Earth's surface

global warming   increase in the world's temperature caused by greenhouse gases in the atmosphere

gravity   the force of attraction on an object by another – usually the Earth

greenhouse gas   gas for example, carbon dioxide or water vapour that is in the atmosphere and contributes to global warming

H

habitat   place where an animal or plant lives

hazard label   warning sign

heart   organ that pumps blood around the body

herbivore   animal that only eats plants

hydrocarbon   contains only carbon and hydrogen

hydrogen   gas that burns with a squeaky 'pop' when lit

hypothermia   when the body gets too cold

I

indicator   chemical that changes colour in acids and alkalis

infrared   radiation beyond the red end of the visible spectrum that is efficient at transferring heat

inherited   characteristic that is passed on from parent to child

insoluble   does not dissolve

insulator   material that does not allow heat to pass through easily

insulin   hormone in the body that controls blood sugar level

interference   waves interacting with each other to reduce the quality of radio and television sound and pictures

L

laser   device that produces a very narrow, intense beam of light

lava   molten rocks erupting from a volcano

lens   part of the eye/a curved piece of transparent material that focuses a beam of light

limewater   solution used to test for carbon dioxide

loudspeaker   a device that changes electrical signals into sound

luminous   produces its own light

M

magma   molten rock in the mantle

magnet   device that can attract iron and steel

magnetic   attracted by a magnet

magnetic field   area around a magnet where the attraction of the magnet is felt

mantle   magma inside the Earth

mapping   represent an area of land and/or obtain directions from one place to another

melanoma   type of skin cancer that appears as a coloured mark or growth on the skin

melt   change from a solid into a liquid

methane   colourless gas used as a fuel

microbe   tiny organism that can only be seen with a microscope

microwave   wave from the electromagnetic spectrum used for cooking and communication

mining   digging out of the ground

molecule   chemical with two or more parts

monomer   small molecules made from crude oil

moon   natural body in space in orbit around a planet

Morse code   code consisting of dots and dashes for each letter of the alphabet

motor   device that converts electricity into movement energy

MRI scanner   device that uses a powerful magnetic field to see inside the body without surgery

N

National Grid   network of electricity cables that distribute electricity across the country

Near Earth Object   any asteroid or comet whose orbit brings it close to Earth

network   a system that allows communication between things like computers or mobile phones

neutral   solution with a pH of 7

neutralisation   when an acid and alkali react to make salt and water

neutron   particle found in the nucleus of an atom

Newton   a unit of force

nicotine   chemical in cigarette smoke that is addictive

nitrogen   an unreactive gas that makes up 79% of the air

nitrogen oxides   pollutants made when fuels burn that cause acid rain and asthma

non-biological   washing powder without enzymes

non-luminous   object that does not produce its own light

Northern Lights   display of lights near the North Pole caused by the interaction between the Earth's magnetic field and cosmic rays from the Sun

nuclear   to do with the nucleus

nucleus   part of the cell that controls the cell

O

observatory   building from which astronomers look at the sky using telescopes

optical fibre   flexible transparent fibre through which light passes by successive internal reflections

orbit   path of a smaller object around a larger object

ores   metal compounds found in the ground

organic farming   growing food without using chemicals

ovary   part of the female body that makes eggs

oxygen   gas that makes up 20% of the air

P

pancreas   organ that makes insulin

parabolic   U-shaped curve with specific properties

particle   very small part of something

pasteurised milk   milk that has been heated to 70 °C for a few seconds to kill harmful microbes

petrol   liquid used as a fuel

pH scale   way to show pH using numbers from 1 to 14

photocell   device which converts light energy into electricity

photosynthesis   when plants use light energy to make food

pigment   the coloured part of paint

planet   large mass of rock which orbits a star

platinum   precious metal/catalyst in a car exhaust

pole   the end of a magnet where the field is concentrated

pollutant   unwanted solid, liquid or gas

polymer   long chain of monomers joined together

pooter   equipment used to suck up small animals

predator   animal that hunts and kills other animals

prey   animal that is hunted by other animals

primary (colour)   one of the three colours from which all other colours can be formed

prism   triangular, transparent object that can separate white light into a spectrum

producer   living thing that can make its own food e.g. plants

protein   type of food needed for growth and repair of cells

pulley   machine that consists of a wheel over which a rope or belt passes

Punnett square   diagram that shows how genes are passed on from parents to child

pure   contains only one thing

Q

quadrat   square frame used to count the plants living in one place

quarrying   digging out from a cliff

R

radar   system which uses radio waves and microwaves to find the position of an object

radiation   energy that travels as a wave and which can pass through space

radio   wave from the electromagnetic spectrum used for communication

radioactive   material which gives out radiation from the break-up of atoms

radiotherapy   treatment of diseases like cancer using radiation

reactants   chemicals used at the start of a reaction

reaction   when particles collide to make a new substance

reaction time   time between receiving a stimulus and responding to it

receptor   nerve cell that detects a stimulus

reflect   rebound from a surface

reflex   when the body reacts automatically to a stimulus to protect the body

refraction   change in direction of light when it passes from one material into another

renewable   source of energy that can be produced as quickly as it is used

repel   to push apart

reprocessed   material that has been used once then changed so that it can be used again

respiration   releasing energy from food

retina   part of the eye that changes light into nerve impulses

rocket   device used to launch a spacecraft

rudder   device mounted on the back of a wind turbine that controls the direction in which the turbine faces

S

satellite   body orbiting around a larger body

sediment   undissolved solid that settles on the bottom

selective breeding   when two organisms are chosen with the desired characteristics and then mated to produce offspring

sensitivity   responding to changes in the environment

skin cancer   cancer that forms in the tissues of the skin

solar powered   the use of energy from the Sun

Solar System   collection of eight planets and other objects orbiting the Sun

soluble   dissolves

solvent   a liquid that solids dissolve in

Space Shuttle   reusable spacecraft

Space Station   spacecraft in orbit around the Earth which is permanently manned

species   group of living organisms that can breed with each other to have offspring that can also breed

spectrum (of light)   the set of colours that appear when white light is separated

star   object in space that produces its own light

sterilised milk   milk heated to 120 °C to kill all the microorganisms

stimulus   change in the environment that the body reacts to

strong acid   acid with a pH of 1, 2 or 3
Sun   star at the centre of our Solar System

T

tail (comet)   the dust from a comet as it passes close to the Sun produced when the ice melts
tectonic plate   section of crust and mantle that carry continents
telescope   combination of lenses and/or mirrors the makes objects appear larger
temporary (magnet)   a magnetised material that loses its magnetism over a short space of time
testes   part of the male body that makes sperm
thermal imaging   the use of a special camera to produce an image based on the temperature of an object
thermochromic   paints that change colour when the temperature changes
thinking distance   distance travelled by a vehicle during the reaction time
thrust   a driving force
tidal barrage   barrier across an estuary which contains turbines to generate electricity as the tide flows in and out
tracer   radioactive substance used in a nuclear medicine scan where movement of a particular chemical is followed in the body
transformer   device which can change the size of a voltage
transparent   material through which it is possible to see clearly
transverse (wave)   wave in which the vibration is at right angles to the direction in which the wave travels
tsunami   very large water wave caused by a disturbance of the Earth's surface
turbine   device that converts movement in a liquid or gas into circular movement to drive a generator

U

ultraviolet   radiation beyond the blue end of the visible spectrum
universal indicator solution   mix of indicators used to measure pH
Universe   everything that exists in space
unreactive   does not make new substances
uranium   radioactive metal used in nuclear power stations

V

vaccination   injection that is given to protect a person from disease
variation   the ways in which members of that same species can be different
vein   blood vessel that takes blood to the heart
virus   microbe that causes certain diseases, for example chicken pox
vitamin   chemical needed by the body to keep healthy
voltage   measure of the amount of energy that produces an electric current

W

waste   any unwanted material
wavelength   the distance between one point on a wave and the next similar point
weak acid   acid with a pH of 4, 5 or 6
wind farm   a collection of wind turbines

X

X-ray   electromagnetic radiation used by doctors to look inside a patient's body

⦀➡ Acknowledgements

The publishers wish to thank the following for permission to reproduce photographs. Every effort has been made to trace copyright holders and to obtain their permission for the use of copyright materials. The publishers will gladly receive any information enabling them to rectify any error or omission at the first opportunity.

Cover & p 1 Mehau Kulyk/Science Photo Library, p 6-7 Triff/Shutterstock, p 8t Rido/Shutterstock, p 8b Kitch Bain/Shutterstock, p 10 Dr Gopal Murti/Science Photo Library, p 11 Jim Kolaczko/iStockphoto, p 13b Gorilla/Shutterstock, p 13t Max Delson Martins Santos/iStockphoto, p 14 Jaimie Duplass/Shutterstock, p 15t iofoto/Shutterstock, p 15b Mikael Damkier/Shutterstock, p 19t iofoto/Shutterstock, p 19b qingqing/Shutterstock, p 20t Arpad Benedek/iStockphoto, p 20b Clive Watkins/Shutterstock, p 21 ILya Afanasiev/iStockphoto, p 22t Linda Bucklin/Shutterstock, p 22b SergeyDV/Shutterstock, p 23t Duncan Walker/iStockphoto, p 23b Khoroshunova Olga/Shutterstock, p 24 pschwarz/Shutterstock, p 25t ILya Afanasiev/iStockphoto, p 25b Mike Price/Shutterstock, p 26t Agita Leimane/iStockphoto, p 26b Royster/Shutterstock, p 27 Andrea Danti/Shutterstock, p 28 withGod/Shutterstock, p 29 Mike Flippo/Shutterstock, p 30t Elena Elisseeva/Shutterstock, p 30b Helder Almeida/Shutterstock, p 31t Royster/Shutterstock, p 31b Michelangelus/Shutterstock, p 32 Andresr/Shutterstock, p 33t Elena Schweitzer/Shutterstock, p 33b africa924/Shutterstock, p 34 ilbusca/iStockphoto, p 37t Foodography/Shutterstock, p 37b c./Shutterstock, p 38t Lisa F. Young/Shutterstock, p 38b Galyna Andrushko/Shutterstock, p 39 salajean/Shutterstock, p 43t Pascal RATEAU/Shutterstock, p 43b Lin, Chun-Tso/Shutterstock, p 44t wavebreakmedia ltd/Shutterstock, p 45 Natursports/Shutterstock, p 46t Pascal Marseaud, ISM/Science Photo Library, p 46b auremar/Shutterstock, p 47 Sebastian Kaulitzki/Shutterstock, p 48 Igor Skrbic/iStockphoto, p 49t Sebastian Kaulitzki/Shutterstock, p 49b Linda Hides/iStockphoto, p 50t kropic1/Shutterstock, p 50b Dgrilla/Shutterstock, p 51l Ludmila Yilmaz/Shutterstock, p 51r EcoPrint/Shutterstock, p 52 mlorenz/Shutterstock, p 53 Leslie Garland Picture Library/Alamy, p 55t loriklaszlo/Shutterstock, p 55b Dag Sjöstrand/iStockphoto, p 56 Yuganov Konstantin/Shutterstock, p 57t Mau Horng/Shutterstock, p 57b Kim Gunkel/iStockphoto, p 58t Kirk Strickland/iStockphoto, p 58b Yuri Arcurs/Shutterstock, p 59 altafulla/Shutterstock, p 61t Konstantin Sutyagin/Shutterstock, p 61b auremar/Shutterstock, p 62 Robert Kneschke/Shutterstock, p 63 Caroline Green/Collins, p 64t Jarno Gonzalez Zarraonandia/Shutterstock, p 64b ilFede/Shutterstock, p 65t F8.IN.TH/Shutterstock, p 65b Eric Isselée/Shutterstock, p 67t Bogdan Wankowicz/Shutterstock, p 67b Csaba Vanyi/Shutterstock, p 68t mangostock/Shutterstock, p 68b James Steidl/Shutterstock, p 69t Sinisa Botas/Shutterstock, p 69b

Adrian Baras/Shutterstock, p 70t devi/Shutterstock, p 70b Monika Wisniewska/Shutterstock, p 71t John Roman Images/Shutterstock, p 71b Geoff Tompkinson/Science Photo Library, p 72 Neustockimages/iStockphoto, p 73t Olaf Speier/Shutterstock, p 73b Aleksandra Nadeina/Shutterstock, p 74t Rob Byron/Shutterstock, p 74b Power and Syred/Science Photo Library, p 75t AISPIX/Shutterstock, p 75b sonya etchison/Shutterstock, p 76 wavebreakmedia ltd/Shutterstock, p 77t Leonid Ikan/Shutterstock, p 77a Poulsons Photography/Shutterstock, p 77b Andy Dean Photography/Shutterstock, p 77c Gelpi/Shutterstock, p 77d Kurhan/Shutterstock, p 79t Sashkin/Shutterstock, p 79b AISPIX/Shutterstock, p 80t Kurhan/Shutterstock, p 80l BioMedical/Shutterstock, p 80c p Hawtin, University of Southampton/Science Photo Library, p 80r Manfred Kage/Science Photo Library, p 80b A. Dowsett, Health Protection Agency/Science Photo Library, p 81t ying/Shutterstock, p 81b ppart/Shutterstock, p 83t Don Bayley/iStockphoto, p 83b Sura Nualpradid/Shutterstock, p 85t Gregory Gerber/Shutterstock, p 85b Dmitry Naumov/iStockphoto, p 86-87 james steidl/iStockphoto, p 88 NataliaYeromina/Shutterstock, p 90 sciencephotos/Alamy, p 93t Andrey Nyunin/Shutterstock, p 93b Andrew Lambert Photography/Science Photo Library, p 94t Willie B. Thomas/iStockphoto, p 94b Peter S/Shutterstock, p 95 AlexRoz/Shutterstock, p 96 Valeriy Velikov/Shutterstock, p 99t Robyn Mackenzie/Shutterstock, p 99b Steshkin Yevgeniy/Shutterstock, p 100 Olker Steger, Peter Arnold Inc/Science Photo Library, p 101t Poznyakov/Shutterstock, p 101b Cordelia Molloy/Science Photo Library, p 102 Alex James Bramwell/Shutterstock, p 103 Hadrian/Shutterstock, p 104 Diego Cervo/Shutterstock, p 105t marema/Shutterstock, p 105b chrisbrignell/Shutterstock, p 106t Iakov Filimonov/Shutterstock, p 106b Michal Vitek/Shutterstock, p 107 Lorelyn Medina/Shutterstock, p 108l Stocksnapper/Shutterstock, p 108r Oleksiy Mark/Shutterstock, p 108c ifong/Shutterstock, p 108b Nataliya Hora/Shutterstock, p 111l Chris leachman/Shutterstock, p 111r Chris leachman/Shutterstock, p 111c PolinaR/Shutterstock, p 111b mypix/Shutterstock, p 112t 36clicks/iStockphoto, p 112b Heidi Brand/Shutterstock, p 113 Niels Quist/Shutterstock, p 114t Digital Storm/Shutterstock, p 114b Serenethos/Shutterstock, p 115t Tek Image/Science Photo Library, p 115b Kurhan/Shutterstock, p 117t thumb/Shutterstock, p 117b Greg Epperson/Shutterstock, p 118t Dmitriy Shironosov/Shutterstock, p 118b Expedition 17 crew/NASA, p 119t vovan/Shutterstock, p 119b Andrew Lambert Photography/Science Photo Library, p 120t Konstantin Sutyagin/Shutterstock, p 120b Marek Mnich/iStockphoto, p 121 Barnaby Chambers/Shutterstock, p 123t Ian Bracegirdle/Shutterstock, p 123b Eliza Snow/iStockphoto, p 124t Michael Pettigrew/iStockphoto, p 124b IDAL/Shutterstock, p 125 garloon/Shutterstock, p 126t fumumpa/iStockphoto, p 126b Baptist/Shutterstock, p 127t Ben Haslam/Haslam Photography/Shutterstock, p 127b jocic/Shutterstock, p 129t Yury Kosourov/Shutterstock, p 129b Dima Kalinin/Shutterstock, p 130t Jeremy Bishop/Science Photo Library, p 130b Sarah Dunn/iStockphoto, p 133 Christian Darkin/Science Photo Library, p 135t Andrea Danti/Shutterstock, p 135b Vulkanette/Shutterstock, p 136 Galyna Andrushko/Shutterstock, p 138 Jerry Sharp/Shutterstock, p 141t Dmitri Melnik/Shutterstock, p 141b Danie van Niekerk/Shutterstock, p 142 hagit berkovich/Shutterstock, p 143 Photobac/Shutterstock, p 144t Iakov Filimonov/Shutterstock, p 144b Picsfive/Shutterstock, p 145 Jaime Pharr/Shutterstock, p 147t Matthew Cole/iStockphoto, p 147b gresei/Shutterstock, p 148t Edw/Shutterstock, p 148b Shawn Hempel/Shutterstock, p 149t Leah-Anne Thompson/Shutterstock, p 149b 67photo/Alamy, p 150 Leah-Anne Thompson/Shutterstock, p 151t Charles D. Winters/Science Photo Library, p 151b PeJo/Shutterstock, p 152 Li Wa/Shutterstock, p 153t corepics/Shutterstock, p 153b Kenneth Sponsler/Shutterstock, p 154 Digital Storm/Shutterstock, p 156t Dave Logan/iStockphoto, p 156b Danny E Hooks/Shutterstock, p 157l INSAGO/Shutterstock, p 157r Norman Pogson/Shutterstock, p 159t photobank.kiev.ua/Shutterstock, p 159b Konstantin Sutyagin/shutterstock, p 160t Guillaume P/Science Photo Library, p 160c Andrew McClenaghan/Science Photo Library, p 160b Science Photo Library, p 161t Robyn Mackenzie/Shutterstock, p 161b MikeE/Shutterstock, p 162t ifong/Shutterstock, p 162b St. Mary's Hospital Medical School/Science Photo Library, p 163t Alex Segre/Alamy, p 163b Natursports/Shutterstock, p 165t Sandra Caldwell/Shutterstock, p 165b Wutthichai/Shutterstock, p 166-167 corepics/Shutterstock, p 168 Aija Lehtonen/Shutterstock, p 169t Anthony Baggett/iStockphoto, p 169b Supri Suharjoto/Shutterstock, p 170t Nejron Photo/Shutterstock, p 170b sciencephotos/Alamy, p 171 MishAl/Shutterstock, p 172 lev dolgachov/Shutterstock, p 173t scyther5/Shutterstock, p 173b AigarsR/Shutterstock, p 174 Dmitry Matrosov/Shutterstock, p 175 Eder/Shutterstock, p 176 stephen mulcahey/Shutterstock, p 177 Can Balcioglu/Shutterstock, p 179t Peteri/Shutterstock, p 179b Scott Hortop/iStockphoto, p 180 Blend Images/Alamy, p 181 Matthew Cole/iStockphoto, p 183t GIPhotostock/Science Photo Library, p 183b dvande/Shutterstock, p 184t Andrew Lambert Photography/Science Photo Library, p 184b Leslie Garland Picture Library/Alamy, p 185t Pi-Lens/Shutterstock, p 185b MilanB/Shutterstock, p 186 courtesy of Reddevilsonline.com, p 187 Matej Michelizza/iStockphoto, p 188t Tomas Skopal/Shutterstock, p 188b Evgeny Murtola/Shutterstock, p 189t NASA, p 189b Michael Dwyer/Alamy, p 190 Germanskydiver/Shutterstock, p 191t Tabitha Patrick/iStockphoto, p 191b Sandra Joseph, Kevin O'Connel/NASA, p 192t R. Gino Santa Maria/Shutterstock, p 192b Samuel Acosta/Shutterstock, p 193t NASA, p 193b Albert Barr/Shutterstock, p 194 Ulrich Willmünder/Shutterstock, p 195 Henrik Jonsson/iStockphoto, p 196 sciencephotos/Alamy, p 197t Franc Podgoršek/iStockphoto, p 197b Sam72/Shutterstock, p 198t NASA,

p 198b NASA, p 199t Oleksiy Maksymenko/Alamy, p 199a NASA, p 199b SSV, MIPL, Magellan Team/NASA, p 199c Ali Ender Birer/Shutterstock, p 199d Viking Project/NASA, p 199e University of Arizona/JPL/NASA, p 199f Space Science Institute/JPL/NASA, p 199g JCElv/Shutterstock, p 199h Diego Barucco/Shutterstock, p 200t Pictorial Press Ltd/Alamy, p 200b NASA, p 201t Viktar Malyshchyts/Shutterstock, p 201l Perov Stanislav/Shutterstock, p 201r Loskutnikov/Shutterstock, p 203t jaimaa/Shutterstock, p 203b Diego Barucco/Shutterstock, p 204 Elena Elisseeva/Shutterstock, p 205t ribeiroantonio/Shutterstock, p 205b easyshoot/Shutterstock, p 206t Worldpics/Shutterstock, p 206b stocknadia/Shutterstock, p 207 Robert Biedermann/Shutterstock, p 208 Rafal Olkis/Shutterstock, p 209t ssuaphotos/Shutterstock, p 209b lafoto/Shutterstock, p 210t David Parker/Science Photo Library, p 210b David Cherepuschak/Alamy, p 211t Goddard Space Flight Center/NASA, p 211b NASA, p 212t Walter G Arce/Shutterstock, p 212b JPL Caltech/NASA, p 213 Philippe Gontier/Eurelios/Science Photo Library, p 215t MarcelClemens/Shutterstock, p 215b David Aleksandrowicz/Shutterstock, p 216t Monkey Business Images/Shutterstock, p 216b duoduo/Shutterstock, p 217 Alan Crawford/iStockphoto, p 218 Petar Ivanov Ishmiriev/Shutterstock, p 219t david pearson/Alamy, p 219b Idealink Photography/Alamy, p 221t Minerva Studio/Shutterstock, p 221b iofoto/Shutterstock, p 222t Carole Gomez/iStockphoto, p 222b craftvision/iStockphoto, p 223t Filipe B. Varela/Shutterstock, p 223l Monkey Business Images/Shutterstock, p 223r Olga Utlyakova/Shutterstock, p 224t ElementalImaging/iStockphoto, p 224b bierchen/Shutterstock, p 225 David Young-Wolff/Alamy, p 226 sciencephotos/Alamy, p 227t Blaj Gabriel/Shutterstock, p 227b Jeremy Davies/iStockphoto, p 228t Alexander Tsiaras/Science Photo Library, p 228b Zirafek/iStockphoto, p 230 Skyscan Photolibrary/Alamy, p 231t US Department of Energy/Science Photo Library, p 231b Brian Robert Marshall/Geograph, p 233t dra_schwartzv/iStockphoto, p 233b vasakkohaline/Shutterstock, p 234t Jim West/Alamy, p 234b Edward Kinsman/Photo Researchers, Inc./Science Photo Library, p 235t Jane McIlroy/Shutterstock, p 236t Levent Konuk/Shutterstock, p 236b Christopher Sherry, p 237t Vadim Balantsev/Shutterstock, p 237b Flashon Studio/Shutterstock, p 239t MilanB/Shutterstock, p 239b Baris Simsek/istockphoto, p 240t Ian Shaw/Alamy, p 240b R. Michael Ballard/Shutterstock, p 241 Joseph Nettis/Science Photo Library, p 242t Monkey Business Images/Shutterstock, p 242b skyhawk/Shutterstock, p 243t BanksPhotos/iStockphoto, p 243b ISM/Science Photo Library, p 245t Yuri Arcurs/Shutterstock, p 245b Jannoon028/iStockphoto.

Answers to questions

Biology

B1 Dead or alive

1 growth, nutrition, movement, reproduction, sensitivity, excretion, respiration
2 to remove waste from the body
3 in the blood
4 heart and blood vessels
5 so when they die doctors know they want to donate their organs
6 to stop decay
7 kidney
8 cytoplasm
9 old cells divide
10 recovery
11 measure resting pulse, exercise, measure pulse every minute until it returns to normal
12 oxygen
13 to contract
14 stop you damaging your muscles
15 **a)** 40 beats per minute; **b)** muscles were working harder so needed more energy from respiration, this means the muscles needed more oxygen, blood is pumped faster to get more oxygen to the muscle.

B2 Babies

1 ovary
2 when egg and sperm fuse
3 oviduct
4 *any two from*: height, blood pressure, weight
5 periods stop
6 identical
7 e.g. high blood pressure could mean the baby is in danger or the mother may get kidney problems
8 oxygen
9 contraction of the muscle wall of the womb
10 afterbirth
11 passes across the placenta into the mother's blood
12 **a)** 4.10 kg; **b)** 0.4 kg
13 *one from*: clean water, building materials, food, fuel, homes
14 does not rot.

B3 Extinction

1 millions, fossils
2 animal dies, soft parts rot, animal gets covered by mud or sand, hard parts turn to stone
3 soft parts rot away
4 too cold
5 3500 million
6 evolution
7 not all species have turned into fossils, some species have no hard body parts so they just rotted away
8 different, shorter, survive
9 food, shelter, mates
10 get away from the fox so are not eaten
11 collect more water from the soil
12 when a species no longer exists on Earth
13 hunting, habitat destruction, pollution
14 **a)** giant panda; **b)** African elephant; **c)** stop hunting, protect habitat, breeding programmes.

B4 Casualty

1 so that the body gets oxygen
2 answer dependent on country
3 include ideas about covering mouth and holding nose, and how to do chest compressions
4 rest, ice, compression, elevate
5 right
6 so it has enough oxygen for the muscles to contract
7 stop the blood going the wrong way,
8 vein
9 capillary
10 more blood could be lost
11 10% of 5 = 0.5 litres
12 eat less fat, exercise, don't smoke
13 chemicals in the smoke make the heart beat quicker, or damage to lungs means heart gets less oxygen
14 **a)** Adil; **b)** Adil, more people were studied, John only studied his granddad.

B5 Healthy eating

1 carbohydrates, fats, proteins, minerals, vitamins, water
2 any three fatty foods
3 depends on student
4 Dan because he does more exercise

5 might damage your body
6 risk of heart disease
7 they don't get enough protein
8 **a)** sugar; **b)** low or only trace of salt
9 blue-black
10 add biuret solution to see if it goes violet
11 mouth, oesophagus, stomach, small intestine, large intestine, rectum, anus
12 stomach
13 small intestine
14 see diagram on page 35 of Student Book.

B6 Control systems

1 37 °C
2 to prevent damage to the body
3 40 °C
4 leads to dehydration
5 when the body gets too cold
6 less blood flow to ears, nose and skin surface, shiver, hairs stand on end
7 more blood flow to skin surface, sweat, hairs lie flat
8 less active, can't heat homes
9 **a)** 800 cm^3; **b)** 850 +100 + 1050 = 2000 cm^3
10 kidney
11 less as water lost in sweat
12 pancreas
13 energy
14 any food high in sugar

B7 Gasping for breath

1 oxygen
2 carbon dioxide, water
3 turns limewater cloudy
4 breath out onto a piece of glass, touch the glass with blue cobalt chloride paper, it should turn pink
5 upwards and outwards, downwards and inwards
6 oxygen goes into the blood, carbon dioxide leaves the blood goes into the air
7 windpipe (trachea)
8 use the apparatus from practical sheet b7_2
9 become narrow
10 reliever and preventer
11 poster should include images of airways, mention breathing problems and smaller lung capacities
12 nicotine
13 carries less oxygen
14 they get the nicotine they crave from the cigarette.

B8 Creepy crawlies

1 leaf
2 carbon dioxide
3 ground
4 no oxygen, no food
5 carnivores, herbivores
6 catch and kill prey
7 camouflaged so can hide from predator
8 tiger needs to judge distance, antelope needs to see all around
9 make their own food
10 blackberries → mice → owl
11 *any two from*: sheep, rabbit, plant-eating insects
12 e.g. heather → rabbits → fox
13 net
14 catch crawling animals
15 **a)** 3 × 500 = 1500; **b)** no, some squares would have no dandelions in them.

B9 Fooling your senses

1 lens – focus, retina – sensitive, optic nerve – takes signals
2 advantage – judge distance, disadvantage – poor field of view
3 brain combines the image from each eye
4 on tongue
5 nose
6 bitter, sweet, sour, salt
7 nose and tongue
8 stimulus, receptors, effectors, response
9 sound
10 to protect them from too much light
11 to stop too much damage to the body
12 *any two from*: pain, temperature, pressure, touch
13 pressure
14 fewer receptors, further apart.

B10 Food factory

1 seeds, tubers, runners, cuttings
2 stored
3 they had two parents
4 clay
5 pH7
6 blueberries, heather
7 cabbages grow better in clay soils at pH8
8 nitrogen – leaves, phosphorus – roots, potassium – fruit
9 add manure, crop rotation
10 **a)** fact; **b)** opinion
11 twice
12 to kill microbes

13 only cows with highest yields are used for breeding

14 sterilised milk heated to 120 °C for 20 minutes, pasteurised heated to 70 °C for 20 seconds.

B11 Drugs in society

1 chemical that has an effect on the mind or body

2 e.g. caffeine, alcohol, aspirin

3 harmful if not used the right way

4 *one from*: nicotine, caffeine, ecstasy

5 pain killers

6 addictive

7 measure pulse, take a drink, measure pulse again: if it goes up the cola contains caffeine

8 *one from*: heroin, methadone, cocaine, ecstasy, LSD, magic mushrooms

9 life

10 helps to stop pain

11 because you could harm another person

12 *any three from*: blurred vision, slurred speech, poor balance, slower reactions

13 liver damage

14 slower reactions means you could have a crash

15 method similar to that on page 71 of the Student Book.

B12 My genes

1 DNA

2 nucleus

3 Males have XY, females have XX

4 tongue rolling, fixed or free ear lobes

5 e.g. height

6 genes – blue eyes, environment – football and accent

7 depends on class

8 it shows up if you have the gene

9 yes

10

	B	B
B	BB	BB
b	Bb	Bb

11 Punnett square should contain b only – all children will have blue eyes

12 it is caused by a faulty gene

13 by taking some fluid from the womb

14 the man on the left, the woman on the right

15 **a)** recessive;

b)

	F	f
F	FF	Ff
f	Ff	ff

B13 Body wars

1 bacteria, viruses, fungi

2 *any two from*: smallpox, AIDS, flu

3 24

4 keep raw and cooked meat apart, cover salad

5 to clean off microbes

6 to kill microbes in the food

7 depends on student

8 *any three from*: skin, stomach acid, mucus and hairs in nose, clotting blood

9 white blood cells engulf microbes and make antibodies

10 only use antibiotics when you need them, finish the treatment

11 antibiotics do not kill viruses

12 safe form of the microbe

13 typhoid, diphtheria, hepatitis A

14 there may be risks

15 not all their reports are completely true.

Chemistry

C1 Acids and alkalis

1 a chemical that changes the colour of a fabric

2 beetroot, red onion, litmus

3 crush the plant, boil to dissolve, filter

4 *any three from*: lemons, limes, vinegar, tea, coffee

5 corrosive, irritant

6 *any three from*: making soap, sticking dyes to fabric, making glass, curing indigestion

7 colourless

8 contain weak acids that are not harmful

9 3 to 4

10 decreases

11 increases

12 checking pH of water in fish farms, any other use in a large outdoor area

13 **a)** limewater; **b)** turns milky white

14 a salt

15 reducing soil pH, curing indigestion.

C2 Cooking and cleaning

1 any two

2 boiling, frying, grilling, steaming, baking, microwaving

3 chemical reactions during cooking

4 improves taste, texture, flavour and makes it easier to digest and kill microbes

5 makes cakes rise

6 carbon dioxide

7 the alcohol evaporates

8 sugar ('yeast' above arrow) à alcohol + carbon dioxide
9 adding alkali to fat or oil
10 the water contains calcium
11 the water-liking heads isolate the greasy blob
12 enzymes
13 **a)** dry clean only; **b)** iron symbol with one dot
14 by providing an active site for a specific reaction to take place.

C3 Colours and smells

1 gives colour
2 binder
3 to dissolve the pigment, keep it liquid, and to evaporate to dry the paint
4 water evaporates and paint dries
5 solvent evaporates and binder hardens
6 solvent is more expensive (than water)
7 gloss
8 oil paint dries when solvent evaporates / watercolour paint dries when water evaporates
9 a liquid that can dissolve a solid
10 will not dissolve
11 particles move faster so hit harder and breaks bits off faster
12 structure prevents water from breaking bits off
13 so the scent can travel
14 **a)** musk; **b)** lavender / rose / orange
15 made by people
16 body heat evaporates the scent, which spreads out into the air and is breathed in
17 weak acid, alcohol.

C4 Heavy metal?

1 in the ground and in rivers
2 *any three from*: unreactive, attractive, shiny, heavy, rare (except expensive)
3 10 g
4 £10 500
5 dipping (in molten metal), electroplating
6 conducting solution
7 stronger than one made of pure gold
8 looks more attractive and reduces cost
9 lightweight, does not corrode
10 advantage, *one from*: saves weight, prevents rusting; disadvantage: not as strong as steel
11 water and oxygen
12 more reactive so higher cost to extract it (accept lower % on Earth)
13 good conductor
14 removal of oxygen
15 carbon
16 saves energy, saves (natural) resources
17 scrap is not pure, so final product is not pure.

C5 Fibres and fabrics

1 by weaving or joining fibres together
2 cotton
3 lightweight and tough
4 non-absorbent, lightweight, tough, rip resistant, transparent section
5 so you can put them on
6 add weights until it snaps
7 keeps sweat in
8 they have very small holes in the fabric that let sweat / water vapour out
9 waterproof suit and seals keep water out, trapped air insulates / reduces heat loss
10 coat with a chemical
11 **a)** borax; **b)** 5 seconds
12 once a week
13 alert people to a fire earlier so they can escape before being overcome by smoke or flames
14 *any three from*: plasters, dressings, bandages, gloves
15 so they do not stretch
16 get an itchy rash
17 to reduce the chance of infection to both casualty and first aider.

C6 Clean air?

1 carbon dioxide
2 oxygen
3 not enough oxygen in the air at altitude
4 air is a mixture of gases, and water in the atmosphere is mainly solid or liquid
5 *Any two from*: coal, oil, gas – accept any other correct fuels
6 **a)** limewater; **b)** turns milky / cloudy / white
7 traps heat in the atmosphere
8 good – keeps planet warn, bad – could get too warm
9 harmful chemicals
10 sulfur dioxide, nitrogen oxides
11 sulfur dioxide and nitrogen oxide gases dissolve in water
12 wind carries pollution made here over to them
13 substance that speeds up a reaction without being used up
14 nitrogen oxides, carbon dioxide, hydrocarbons
15 every year
16 it must have another oxygen added.

C7 Strong stuff

1 hard 1
2 flexible
3 insulated, coloured to tell them apart
4 most of its properties match those in the non-metal list

5 alloy it
6 brass
7 return to original shape when heated
8 rub two materials together
9 bend a wire made of it, place in hot water and see if it changes back
10 mining, quarrying
11 made in a standard regular shape
12 concrete with steel cage / bars in it
13 Students' own plans
14 mass and volume
15 advantage – strong, disadvantage – heavy (accept rusts)
16 **a)** cycle shelter, boat hull; **b)** loft boarding, boat panels; **c)** bridges, buildings, roads
17 combine useful properties of different materials.

C8 Restless Earth

1 liquid rock
2 crust
3 earthquakes and volcanoes (accept mountains)
4 answer depends on year in which question is tackled – in 2012 it will be 4.88 m
5 energy, shock wave
6 smaller earthquakes
7 large wave caused by an underwater earthquake
8 match the names of the plates given to the map on page 130 of the Student Book
9 magma is underground / lava is magma exposed to the air
10 lava, ash, gases
11 every eruption adds more lava and ash layers
12 by pulling apart leaving gaps, or one plate sinking and melting magma, which is released
13 the movement of whole continents
14 continents fit together, similar fossils and rock types on different continents
15 satellite data and magnetic measurements
16 evidence.

C9 How fast? How slow?

1 explosions, fireworks
2 measure mass change, measure volume change
3 reactants get used up
4 reactions stats quickly, then slows, then stops
5 **a)** increases it; **b)** more collisions
6 **a)** increases it; **b)** more collisions
7 half the mass, or double the water
8 it's the only place particles can collide
9 increases
10 causes explosions

11 greater surface area, so faster reaction
12 speed up reactions, not used up, only need a small amount
13 **a)** copper sulphate; **b)** not the right catalyst for this reaction
14 15 minutes
15 provides a site for the reactants to fit into or onto.

C10 Sorting out

1 substances are not joined
2 properties of the substances in it
3 filtering
4 add to water, stir, filter, evaporate the filtrate
5 **a)** E102; **b)** E131
6 iron, steel, cobalt, nickel
7 use a magnet
8 dissolve at different rates
9 so the solid is left behind
10 *any one from*: separating blood cells or other cells, isolating viruses
11 salts
12 centrifuging separates suspended solids, decanting separates settled solids
13 if it boils at 100 °C and freezes at 0 °C
14 carbon
15 evaporation and condensation
16 heat to 78 °C so the alcohol evaporates, cool the vapour into a liquid.

C11 CSI plus

1 Scene Of Crime Officer
2 *any four from*: hair, fibre, dandruff, soil, tyre imprint, fingerprint, DNA
3 to prevent contamination / so it can be matched to a particular place
4 cannot be used for evidence in court
5 wipe / rub them away
6 arch, loop, whorl
7 16
8 quicker to check against previous records, available nationally for matching
9 carry oxygen
10 O, A, B, AB
11 O
12 correct bar chart drawn
13 dissolved
14 a chemical carrying the genetic code
15 when it is incomplete or contaminated
16 dissolve a sample from the suspect area, and a sample from another area, but a spot on chromatography paper, stand in water so spots above water, leave, see if the dyes are different.

C12 Fuels

1 dark, sticky, toxic liquid
2 carbon and hydrogen
3 250 to 300°C
4 Bar chart correctly drawn
5 (fractional) distillation
6 small molecules
7 electricity
8 they have lower boiling points so stay as gases at lower temperatures
9 *any three from*: same sized container, same amount of water heated, same start temperature, fuel burnt for same time, flame same size and distance
10 when a fuel burns in a limited air supply
11 detector, have gas appliances serviced
12 in a lot, carbon dioxide is made, in a bit carbon monoxide and carbon are made
13 49.8 mpg
14 diesel by 70 dB
15 petrol
16 diesel: costs more to buy but more mpg, more time between servicing, lasts for over 100 000 miles; petrol: needs servicing more often but cheaper to buy, better acceleration, fuel a bit cheaper.

C13 What's added to our food?

1 chemicals added to food
2 antioxidant
3 Epi-pen / adrenaline
4 only tested on a sample of people
5 spoil it
6 *any three from*: limes, lemons, apple, tomatoes, carrots, blackberries, grapes – accept others that have been taught
7 to keep them crispy and dry
8 cells (cell walls) are cut, allowing contents to react with oxygen in the air
9 to stay healthy
10 to make sure people get enough vitamins in their diet
11 sweetener, preservative
12 for energy (respiration), too much can cause medical problems (obesity / type 2 diabetes)
13 flavouring, preservative
14 high blood pressure, heart attacks
15 subsidence, damage to crops, environmental damage
16 to remind people they need to limit the salt, sugar and fats they eat, and to try to make it easier for people understand how much are in foods.

Physics

P1 Getting the message

1 satnav
2 can be used anywhere
3 message from radio and message through air
4 300 000 km/s
5 text / use hands-free / limit talk time
6 for – more people closer to mast; against – possible risk to schoolchildren
7 *any two from*: light waves, infrared, microwaves, radio waves ·
8 distance between one point on wave and next similar point ·
9 **a)** amplitude / loudness · **b)** higher frequency / pitch ·
10 *one from*: better sound / picture quality, less interference, electronic programme guide, interactive, more choice ·
11 digital so not affected by interference ·
12 science is fun to do.

P2 Our electricity supply

1 400 000 V
2 230 V
3 needs different metals / potato not acidic
4 formed from fossilised remains
5 turn the generator
6 27%
7 change size of voltage
8 3.9513 kWh
9 in town to reduce high voltage to 230 V
10 13.65p
11 *any three from*: curtains, curtain lining, blinds, double glazing
12 cavity wall insulation.

P3 Attractive forces

1 north pole, south pole
2 stroke it with a magnet
3 they are magnetised
4 along a N–S line
5 *any two from*: affect electronic circuits / damage health (cataracts, increased cancer risk) / affect cloud formation
6 north
7 no atmosphere between them and cosmic rays
8 becomes louder
9 see student text
10 stronger
11 not rigidly fixed
12 coil wire around an iron core
13 increase current / increase turns on coil

14 *one from*: sorting metal / MRI scan / moving cars in scrapyard

15 the paper clips stay on the electromagnet.

P4 Pushes and pulls

1 54 m/s
2 speeds up
3 air resistance suddenly increases
4 rubber
5 stretches
6 it goes back to its original length
7 it is very elastic and stretches a lot so that the jumper does not slow down in a short space of time
8 *any two from*: speed cameras, chicanes, speed humps
9 stretches to reduce force of impact
10 changes its shape
11 110 km/h
12 exhaust gases being forced out very quickly
13 water being forced out very quickly
14 burn up in atmosphere
15 *one from*: cost, less time to prepare for launch.

P5 Let there be light!

1 yellow
2 cyan
3 these colours are primary colours and can make any other colour
4 *any two from*: star, named star, flame, lit bulb
5 anything else
6 6000–10 000 °C
7 eyes produce light
8 *one from*: laser beams are straight, shadow edges are sharp
9 appears back to front
10 changes direction
11 diagram as student text / angles both labelled 50°
12 *any two from*: spectacles for long sight, projector, camera, telescope, magnifying glass
13 reflected
14 speed of light
15 smaller diameter cable for same number of telephone calls / less signal loss so fewer amplifiers needed / cleared signal / no corrosion.

P6 Final frontier

1 oxygen, food, water
2 telescope
3 no light pollution, no dust in atmosphere
4 8
5 Jupiter

6 increases
7 Venus
8 it orbits the Sun
9 Jupiter
10 Uranus
11 closest body to Earth
12 Milky Way
13 Earth is at the edge of the galaxy
14 100 000 years
15 take too long.

P7 Alternative energy

1 non-renewable sources will run out one day, renewable ones won't
2 Sun
3 760
4 *one from*: used in remote locations, no lengthy power leads
5 darkness
6 black
7 we have sunlight but not high temperatures
8 flour, energy
9 does not depend on wind direction
10 rudder / blades change angle
11 they think they will spoil scenery
12 energy from plant and animal waste
13 burning, fermentation
14 source always there
15 needs large tidal range.

P8 Deep impacts

1 near Earth object
2 meteors burn up in space, meteorites pass through the atmosphere and land on Earth
3 no plants for herbivores to eat so they died out, no animals for carnivores to eat so they died out
4 the Sun
5 nearly 1000 km
6 away from the Sun
7 2061
8 crater
9 200 million years
10 collision between two planets, rocks thrown out formed Moon
11 have same origin
12 telescopes
13 less light pollution
14 can do more damage if they collide with Earth
15 340 000 km approximately.

P9 Driving along

1 to save fuel, improve safety
2 15 m

3 more likely to have to stop quickly in a town
4 petrol, diesel
5 to ignite petrol vapour
6 60 km/h
7 to record distance travelled in given time
8 wheel and axle, pulley, gear
9 steering wheel, road wheels
10 driver
11 2.5
12 batteries
13 *one from*: free energy, no polluting waste, no effect on fossil fuel stocks
14 brushes touching contacts
15 reverses current direction in the coil every half turn.

P10 Hot stuff!

1 to reduce convection
2 *one from*: cuts energy bills, reduces carbon dioxide emissions, preserves stocks of fossil fuels
3 more energy lost through the walls than windows
4 joules
5 *any two from*: heating, cooking, generating electricity
6 temperature
7 "Don't let the heat out"
8 change from solid to liquid, liquid to gas, vice versa
9 6 minutes
10 liquid to gas
11 labels on gradients left to right – solid, liquid, gas, liquid, solid
12 curved
13 *one from*: cooking, generating electricity
14 *one from*: free energy, no pollution
15 easier to rotate the smaller mirrors to track the Sun.

P11 Nuclear power

1 to check radiation exposure
2 *any three from*: keep distance, handle with tongs, reduce exposure time, shielding, protective clothing, clear labelling
3 if an accident occurs there is no cover-up
4 magnet
5 decreases
6 rotor coils
7 magnet is not rotating
8 uranium
9 steam

10 advantage – no CO_2, SO_2 emissions / less water vapour / disadvantages – problems of radiation leak in accident
11 students' individual responses
12 special land fill sites
13 molten glass
14 rail
15 represented the waste to see if they were damaged.

P12 Full spectrum

1 heat
2 burglar alarms
3 bonnet and tyres will show up as hot
4 300 000 km/s
5 yellow
6 *any three from*: gamma, X-rays, ultraviolet, visible, infrared, microwaves, radio
7 red
8 can cause blindness
9 bar-code readers
10 to change radio waves into an electrical signal
11 increased speed and quantity of data transmitted
12 microwave
13 clouds and rainfall
14 do not pass through the Earth's atmosphere
15 use for limited periods, text instead of speaking.

P13 Medical rays

1 *one from*: sunburn, skin cancer
2 cover up, use sunscreen, reduce exposure time
3 300 minutes
4 with ultraviolet lamp
5 naturally occurring radiation that is always present
6 *any three from*: gamma, X-rays, ultraviolet, visible light, infrared, microwaves, radio
7 mildly sick
8 see inside body without surgery
9 white
10 X-rays pass through soft tissue
11 diagnosis – finding out what is wrong, treatment – putting right what is wrong
12 liquid, the passage of which can be monitored from outside the body
13 stand behind thick walls
14 gamma radiation is more penetrating
15 radiotherapy – treating with gamma radiation, chemotherapy – treating with chemicals.